//FUEL CELLS//

A SURVEY

By
Bernard J. Crowe

Prepared under Contract NASW-2173 by
COMPUTER SCIENCES CORPORATION
Falls Church, Virginia

DONATION 4/79

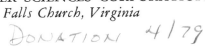

Technology Utilization Office 1973
NATIONAL AERONAUTICS AND SPACE ADMINISTRATION
Washington, D.C.

For sale by the Superintendent of Documents
U.S. Government Printing Office, Washington, D.C. 20402
Price: 85 cents, domestic postpaid; 60 cents, GPO Bookstore
Stock No. 13300-00500
Library of Congress Catalog Card Number 72-600266

Foreword

Fuel cells, known in principle for over 100 years, are today being used or considered for a variety of tasks. They have been applied as power for automotive purposes, in a submarine, and to meet aerospace requirements. They have actual or potential advantages such as freedom from toxic exhaust emissions, relatively quiet operation, basic simplicity, and high efficiency.

This book is an attempt to discuss fuel cells factually, and to describe their current status; many of the advances in technology have been carried out under NASA sponsorship. Problems as well as potentials are considered, and the changes with the use of various fuels are looked at. Potential users should be aware that there are no magic answers, yet fuel cells are a power source that could be more widely used.

This is one of a series of publications dealing with specialized processes from the standpoint of their applications and methodology. It is part of a program established by the National Aeronautics and Space Administration to collect the results of aerospace-related research and to evaluate, organize and disseminate those results for the benefit of the industrial, educational, and public communities of the Nation. The new technology so collected, and prepared for appropriate audiences, is described and announced in suitable documents, or by other means, and is so made available to potential users. This is the function of the Technology Utilization program, which is characterized by a user-oriented approach in its activities.

References to specific work, and to companies working on or with fuel cells, are provided for the reader who would like to delve into this area of technology. It is hoped that the information will be of value to those interested in developing or using fuel cells.

Director
Technology Utilization Office

III

Acknowledgments

Many individuals assisted in the preparation of this survey, supplying material for inclusion or reviewing the draft. The author extends his thanks to: David Bell, III, G. D. Hydrick, Fulton M. Plauche, and W. Eugene Rice, NASA Manned Spacecraft Center; Leonard Berkowitz, Esso Research and Engineering Company; Richard J. Boehme, Charles Graff, and John R. Morgan, NASA Marshall Space Flight Center; Lloyd E. Chapman and Frank O'Brien, General Electric Company; Ernst M. Cohn, NASA Headquarters; Warren Danzenbaker and Elliot Sivowitch, Smithsonian Institution; Robert W. Easter, Harvey J. Schwartz, and Lawrence H. Thaller, NASA Lewis Research Center; Charles L. Fruchter, Computer Sciences Corporation; Dr. Jose Giner and Dr. Gerhard L. Holleck, Tyco Laboratories, Inc.; Lawrence Handley and William E. Podolny, Pratt and Whitney Aircraft; Joseph H. Karshner, General Motors Corporation; Dr. Karl V. Kordesch and Dr. Robert Powers, Union Carbide Corporation; Larry Rolufs, IRS; and Quentin J. O. Sullivan, Allis-Chalmers.

Illustrations used in the survey were provided by courtesy of Allis-Chalmers (figs. 5 and 6); American Institute of Chemical Engineers (fig. 31); Communications Satellite Corporation (fig. 35); General Electric Company (Figs. 15, 25-29, 37-39); General Motors Corporation (figs. 53-56); Marine Technology Society Journal (figs. 30, 43); A. R. Poirier and AIAA (fig. 33); Pratt and Whitney Aircraft (figs. 20, 23, 24, 36, 40, 41, 48, 49, 51, 52); Tyco Laboratories, Inc. (figs. 46, 47); and Union Carbide Corporation (figs. 57-63).

IV

Contents

CHAPTER 1

Summary

INTRODUCTION

When Sir William Grove demonstrated the first fuel cell in 1839, it must have seemed to some observers that the event heralded the dawn of a new era in the generation of electricity, accompanied as it was by Becquerel's almost simultaneous discovery of the photovoltaic effect. Yet it was over 100 years before Francis Thomas Bacon produced a fuel cell capable of generating useful amounts of power, and another 25 years elapsed before the fuel cell was put to practical use.

Paradoxically, the fuel cell's first utility roles could hardly have been more exotic; namely, providing electrical power for manned exploration of the oceans and space. Indeed, it was the requirements of these exotic missions that made the fuel cell a competitive power-generation candidate for the first time in the face of opposition from hitherto superior techniques. In applications such as these, the fuel cell's unusual characteristics made it a cost-effective solution to problems peculiar to the hostile environments encountered.

To satisfy the requirements of such applications, the fuel cell concept was subjected to an intensive research and development effort during the last decade. This largely NASA-sponsored effort has taken the fuel cell from the status of a demonstration device to that of a sophisticated source of electrical power. Investigators and technologists seek to apply current developments in this field to a number of other, though admittedly less exotic, terrestrial applications. Among the potential advantages claimed for the device are high efficiency, quiet and trouble-free operation, and freedom from toxic and pollutant exhaust emissions.

Why then is the fuel cell not in common use? Surely such an uncommon energy-conversion system has innumerable applications? Answers to these questions form the topics of this book.

ABOUT THIS BOOK

This book is a survey of fuel cell technology and applications; it does not deal with conventional galvanic cells or "storage batteries," nor with hybrids such as the zinc-air battery, which is half fuel cell, half battery. It is not a text book on fuel cells, although references to sources of information are provided for those who wish to know more about the theory, electrochemistry, and design of these useful devices.

The primary goal is to acquaint the reader with the fuel cell, its operating principles, its performance capabilities and its limitations. Most importantly, a number of applications are considered to show how and why different types of fuel cells are best suited to certain roles. The purpose of the survey is to make available accumulated experiences in fuel cell technology, many of which have resulted from research and development programs supported by NASA, and to show how this technology might be put to use in down-to-earth applications.

HOW DO FUEL CELLS WORK?

Like the familiar dry cell and lead-acid batteries, fuel cells work by virtue of electrochemical reactions in which the molecular energy of a fuel and an oxidant are transformed into direct current electrical energy.

Unlike batteries, however, fuel cells do not consume chemicals that form part of their structure or are stored within the structure; the reactants are supplied from outside the cell. Since the fuel cell itself does not undergo an irreversible chemical change, it can continue to operate as long as its fuel and oxidant are supplied and products removed, or at least until the electrodes cease to operate because of mechanical or chemical deterioration. In comparison with a conventional battery, this period of operation may be a significantly longer time.

A fuel cell is represented schematically in figure 1. It consists of a container of electrolyte, in this case a water solution of potassium hydroxide, KOH. In it are immersed two porous electrodes, and through these the reactants, in this example hydrogen and oxygen, are brought into contact with the electrolyte. The hydrogen and oxygen react to release ions and electrons, and water is produced. The electrons are made to do useful work in an external circuit, whereas the ions flow from one electrode to the other to complete the internal circuit in the cell.

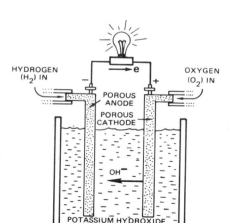

FIGURE 1.–Representation of a simple fuel cell.

If the hydrogen and oxygen were simply mixed as gases at room temperature, then, of course, no reaction would take place. Raising the temperature of the mixture would cause an explosion, liberating some of the energy in the mixture in a very short period of time and releasing it mainly as heat. The fuel cell is a device in which conditions are created to enable the controlled release of this energy. Exactly how this is accomplished is described in Chapter 3.

WHAT ARE THE ADVANTAGES OF FUEL CELLS?

As we have seen, fuel cells convert chemical energy into electrical energy. Of course they are not unique in this respect; a diesel-generator set, for example, does the same thing. The importance of the fuel cell is in the way in which it effects this conversion.

This is represented schematically in figure 2. The diesel-generator converts chemical energy into heat, heat into mechanical motion, and mechanical motion into electricity. The fuel cell performs a one-step, direct transformation of chemical energy into electricity, and although heat is given off in the process it does not constitute an essential link in the energy-conversion chain. Because

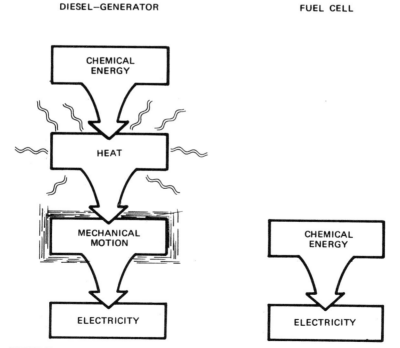

FIGURE 2.—Comparison of energy transformation processes in a diesel generator and a fuel cell.

it bypasses these intermediate steps, the fuel cell does not suffer the energy losses characteristic of thermomechanical devices such as the diesel engine. Consequently, more available fuel energy may be converted into useful electrical energy and as a result, the fuel cell may be more efficient. Because the reaction takes place chemically, the elementary fuel cell has no moving parts to cause vibration and noise. In practice, pumps and other small mechanical units are often required as auxiliaries to the cell, but in general fuel cells run more smoothly and quietly than other power-generation devices.

Perhaps the most important advantage of the fuel cell is that its combustion products are often lower in volume and less hazardous than those from the internal combustion engine. Potentially, the fuel cell is a clean, nonpolluting source of electrical energy. In today's world of ecological awareness and environmental concern, this is an important attribute.

WHY AREN'T FUEL CELLS IN WIDESPREAD USE?

With all these advantages, why aren't fuel cells being used in widespread practical applications?

The answer lies largely in the relative immaturity of the fuel cell as a practical power-conversion device. To be sure, fuel cells have provided our astronauts with life-sustaining electrical power from here to the Moon and back again. But it is only in the last 10 years that such things have become possible and the fuel cell has been significantly understood. The automobile engine, the electric generator, and the battery have all been around for a much longer period. They are in an advanced stage of development and are produced in large quantities. The fuel cell, on the other hand, is still very much in a developmental stage and has never been produced in quantities of more than a few dozen at a time. In comparison with these older devices the fuel cell is prohibitively expensive for many applications.

Cost is not the only block. The fuel cells that powered the Gemini and Apollo spacecraft used pure hydrogen and oxygen as their sources of energy. To be of use on earth, many feel that fuel cells must be capable of using fuels that are more readily available, easier to handle, less expensive, and less hazardous. However, there is disagreement about which fuels meet these requirements and which are best for each application. Converting the classic hydrogen-oxygen cell to use any other fuel raises many problems. Lifetime, maintainability, and reliable unattended operation are other problems that must be solved before the fuel cell can take its place beside more familiar devices in day-to-day operation. In chapter 5 we will look at these problems in detail and examine some of the variants of the basic hydrogen-oxygen fuel cell.

WHERE DOES THE FUEL CELL STAND TODAY?

Despite the myriad technical problems confronting the engineer in his attempts to adapt the fuel cell to prosaic tasks, some progress has been made. In remote locations, fuel cells are powering radio relay stations and beacons. In military situations, fuel cells that can run on an extraordinary range of common fuels provide power for communications and other apparatus. Around the United States fuel cells are on shakedown trials in homes, apartments, shops, and factories producing electricity directly from natural gas. In Cleveland an automobile powered by a fuel cell/battery combination carries its designer to and from work each day. And in the laboratory, a fuel cell is being developed that might some day be implanted in the body of a man or woman to power an artificial heart.

The enthusiasm of the 1960's which saw the fuel cell as a panacea to many social ills has given way in the seventies to cautious optimism—an optimism which sees potential uses for fuel cells on many fronts, but which recognizes the many problems to be solved before that potential can be realized. This, then, appears to be an appropriate time to review fuel cell technology.

CHAPTER 2

Development of the Fuel Cell

INTRODUCTION

It is natural to think of the fuel cell as a product of twentieth century technology, since it has achieved prominence only in the last 10 years. However, the fuel cell concept dates back to the mid-1800's when, it is generally agreed, the first recorded demonstration of the principle was made by Sir William Grove (ref. 1), an English scientist working in the youthful field of electricity. Grove was famous in his lifetime as the inventor of a relatively conventional galvanic cell or "battery" that became known as the Grove Cell (ref. 2). His work on fuel cells was not recognized until much later.

An excursion into the field of electrolysis apparently led Grove to his discovery of the fuel cell principle. He reasoned that if electricity decomposed water into hydrogen and oxygen, then it might be possible to arrange the synthesis of water from its components so as to generate electricity. In his classic experiment reported in 1839 (ref. 1), Grove constructed the first known fuel cell, noting that it produced only a small current. In 1842, he built a bank of 50 such cells and called it a "gaseous voltaic battery" (ref. 3). Each electrode of 1/4-inch platinized platina foil was covered by a glass tube and immersed in dilute sulfuric acid. Alternate tubes contained hydrogen and oxygen (fig. 3).

In a graphic description of the effects produced by his battery, Grove noted: "A shock was given which could be felt by five persons joining hands, and which when taken by a single person was painful." His insight into the mechanisms of the cell was remarkable; Grove clearly recognized the desirability of high-surface area electrodes, but elected not to construct them because of the difficulties involved. Although his battery worked, it was not capable of delivering significant power when compared with more conventional galvanic cells, and he shortly abandoned this line of research. Perhaps the fuel cell's potential for continuous operation did not occur to Grove. In any event, such an attribute probably would not have appeared significant, for most galvanic cells were beset with corrosion problems. Since the materials of the cell could be expected to have only a short life, there was little point in providing a continuous supply of reactants, especially when these were rare and expensive gases.

As a result, 50 years elapsed before any significant advance was made on Grove's "gaseous battery." In 1889 Mond and Langer (ref. 4) constructed a similar device using perforated platinum electrodes catalized by platinum

8 FUEL CELLS

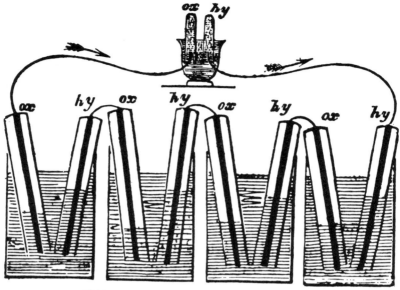

FIGURE 3.—First fuel cell as depicted by Grove.

black. Their cell developed 1-1/2 watts at 50 percent efficiency, demonstrating the value of high-area electrodes. They called it a "fuel cell."

THE FIRST PRACTICAL FUEL CELL

Throughout the first half of the 20th century, several attempts were made to build fuel cells that would convert coal or carbon directly into electricity. Considering the extent of knowledge at that time, it is hardly surprising that none succeeded in producing a really practical power source.

Then, in 1932 Francis T. Bacon, an engineer at Cambridge University in England and a descendant of the famous 17th century scientist, embarked on a development project that was to have a major impact on the future of fuel cells. He selected the hydrogen-oxygen cell with alkaline electrolyte as a practical starting point from which to build a simple demonstration model. Reasoning that the expensive platinum catalysts used by Grove and by Mond and Langer would prohibit the entry of such a cell into the commerical market, Bacon elected to use relatively inexpensive metallic nickel electrodes which were found to be active catalytically at somewhat elevated temperatures.

He soon found that if the cell temperature was raised to about 205° C. (400° F.), the electrochemical reaction rate increased sufficiently to produce useful currents without any additional catalyst. To prevent boiling of the electrolyte, he had to raise the pressure of the system until it was above the water vapor pressure of the potassium hydroxide solution at 205° C. (400° F.).

He then discovered that increasing the pressure resulted in a significant performance increase, so he increased the pressure well above that required to prevent boiling, operating the system at about 414 N/cm^2 (600 psi).

Bacon encountered many problems in developing electrodes with a sufficiently large active area. One of the biggest problems was maintaining a stable interface between the gas and the liquid. He solved this problem by using porous electrodes made in two layers, one layer having a considerably greater pore size than the other. With the gas on the coarse-pore side of the electrode and the electrolyte on the fine-pore side, the interface position was controlled by adjusting the pressure differential between gas and electrolyte.

Although his work was interrupted by World War II, Bacon's persistence enabled him to construct what is generally agreed to be the first useful fuel cell (fig. 4). By the middle of the century he was able to demonstrate a 5-kilowatt (kW) system capable of powering a welding machine, a circular saw, and a 2-ton capacity fork lift truck.

Bacon's demonstration, and the work of others during this period, heralded an explosive growth in fuel cell research in the early 1960's. After 120 years of uncertain progress, the fuel cell began to emerge from the laboratory. Developments occurred rapidly and numerous demonstrations were staged to illustrate the many applications of the device. Among those that received considerable publicity were several developed by the Allis-Chalmers Manufacturing Company (fig. 5) between 1959 and 1963. The apparent sudden succes of the fuel cell and the attendant publicity led to overestimation and overselling of its capabilities as a cure for many domestic, economic, and technical ills. Those working on a fuel cell development recognized only too

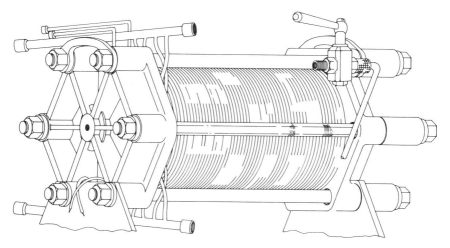

FIGURE 4.—Bacon's high-pressure fuel cell.

FIGURE 5.—Early fuel cell-powered demonstration vehicles.

well the many problems to be solved in building and producing an economical device.

However, not all the fuel cells built at that time were demonstration "toys." In 1964 Allis-Chalmers, under contract to General Dynamics' Electric Boat Division, produced a 750-watt fuel cell system to power a one-man underwater research vessel. Running on liquid hydrazine-hydrate and gaseous oxygen, this powerplant is considered the first practical application of the fuel cell for motive power (fig. 6).

Moreover, the research climate in America at that time strongly favored emerging technologies that might support the developing manned space program. This program was to give significant impetus to the development of the fuel cell and to lead to the solution of many of its teething problems.

NASA IMPETUS TO FUEL CELL DEVELOPMENT

In 1958, as the first U.S. satellite went into orbit, it was realized that the weight and relatively short life of the storage batteries serving its small power requirements would severely hamper extended flights. On subsequent unmanned spacecraft this problem was solved by using solar cells converting the sun's light to electricity by the photovoltaic effect, a phenomenon discovered, curiously enough, by Becquerel at about the time Grove discovered the fuel cell principle. However, for manned space flights the need to point these solar cells at the sun was a disadvantage. The mission times anticipated (7 to 14 days) were too long for primary (nonrechargeable) batteries but short enough to make candidates other than solar cells attractive (fig. 7).

In the process of selecting a power system to meet these requirements, all known solar-, nuclear-, and chemical-conversion techniques were investigated individually, with appropriate combinations of individual systems also considered. Many proposed systems were studied and rated with respect to weight, reliability, safety, power capability, and tolerance to the mission environmental

FIGURE 6.–STAR I, a one-man submarine research and test vessel built in 1964, was powered by a 750-watt hydrazine-oxygen fuel cell designed by Allis-Chalmers. The vessel was the first fuel cell-powered submersible and one of the first practical applications of the fuel cell.

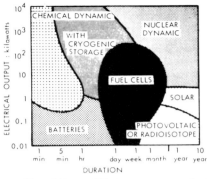

FIGURE 7.—Optimum operation for various energy-conversion devices, circa 1964.

profile. All candidates were required to have known improvement potential that could be realized early in the development program.

It soon was discovered that the fuel cell system offered many advantages, for example, absolute independence with respect to sunlight, aerodynamic forces, and sea level pressure. The high operational efficiency of the fuel cell as compared with conventional heat engines permitted the added advantage of low specific fuel consumption and a lower heat rejection requirement. Because potable water is a byproduct of its electrochemical process, the hydrogen-oxygen fuel cell could also supply water for crew consumption and humidification of cabin air. The fuel cell system was selected finally on the basis of these advantages and others, such as its development status, low system effective weight, and mission flexibility. The absence of solar arrays simplified launch preparations and rendezvous requirements for spacecraft attitude control.

As a result of this decision, NASA funded an extensive research and development program aimed at solving or understanding some of the basic problems and mechanisms of the fuel cell. More than 200 contracts were let to industries and universities to study the basic physics, kinetics, electrochemistry, and catalysis of the fuel cell reaction; to develop methods of making electrodes, retaining electrolytes, removing byproducts, and constructing workable cells; and to investigate several promising approaches to the construction of a practical power-generation system.

The fuel cell technology developed by Bacon in England was one of the approaches investigated. Through the British National Research and Development Council and Leesona-Moos Laboratories, Pratt & Whitney Aircraft acquired the patent to Bacon's fuel cell design in 1959. This technology was to form the basis for the Apollo power plant and help take the first man to the Moon.

But before Apollo, the U.S. astronauts would develop their skills and technology on the Gemini series of earth-orbiting missions. Here too, the fuel cell was to play a crucial role in supplying electrical power during space missions longer than any undertaken at that time and not exceeded until well into the manned lunar exploration phase of Apollo. However, the technology of the cell itself was quite different from Bacon's, relying on a special membrane disclosed by W. T. Grubb in 1957 (ref. 5).

How the Fuel Cell Works

UNDERSTANDING THE FUEL CELL

In considering the fuel cell for any application, it is necessary to appreciate the limitations of the device and the differences between one type of cell and another. A fundamental requirement for such an appreciation is an understanding of the fuel cell and its operation.

Understanding the principle of operation of the fuel cell is not difficult. It does not require an extensive knowledge of chemistry, thermodynamics, or electricity, and the reader does not have to be versed in mathematics or catalysis. Although knowledge of these and related subjects is a prime requirement for electrochemists and technologists who design and develop fuel cells, understanding the basic mechanisms involved, appreciating the losses inherent in these mechanisms, and knowing how those losses may be reduced or negated demand no specialized knowledge or skills.

PRINCIPLE OF OPERATION

The essential features of a single fuel cell are represented in figure 8. In this example, hydrogen and oxygen are the fuel and oxidizer, respectively, and the

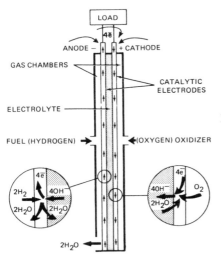

FIGURE 8.—Basic operation of the fuel cell.

electrolyte is a solution of potassium hydroxide. Other cells may use different reactants and/or different electrolytes; however, the salient characteristics of most cells are quite similar and our example serves to illustrate the general principles of operation.

The cell consists essentially of a pair of electrodes separated by an electrolyte. The reactants (in this case, gases) are fed through the porous electrodes and brought into contact with the electrolyte. Reactions take place that set up voltages, or electrical pressures, at the electrodes. When an external load is connected to the electrodes, these voltages drive electrons through the load and perform useful work. In the electrolyte solution, ions travel from one electrode to the other to complete the electrical circuit.

To understand the cell's special features that make these reactions possible, we must look more closely at the electrodes and at the processes that take place there.

ELECTRODE REACTIONS

Hydrogen is fed to the anode and diffuses through the porous, conducting electrode structure until it comes into contact with the electrolyte. The potassium hydroxide electrolyte is rich in hydroxyl (OH^-) ions. At the point where it meets the electrolyte, hydrogen adsorbs upon the electrode surface in an atomic form which renders it highly reactive. The hydrogen atoms react with the hydroxyl ions to form water; and as a result of this reaction, free electrons are left on the anode. The reaction may be represented by the equation:

$$\text{Anode} + H_2 + 2OH^- \rightarrow (\text{Anode} + 2e^-) + 2H_2O$$

Electrons accumulate at the electrode/electrolyte interface where they attract a corresponding quantity of positive ions (in this case, potassium ions, K^+) in the electrolyte solution. A potential energy barrier prevents the positive ions from reaching the electrode surface, so that an opposing layer of electrons and positive ions is set up close to the surface (fig. 9). These layers of charge act in a similar manner to those on the plates of a capacitor, and the potential gradient thus created is part of the essential "driving force" of the fuel cell.

At the cathode, oxygen reacts with the water in the electrolyte to form hydroxyl ions. During this reaction, electrons are removed from the cathode, resulting in a positive charge. The potential difference between the cathode and the adjacent electrolyte supplements the overall cell potential, as shown in figure 10. The reaction at the cathode may be expressed as:

$$(\text{Cathode} + 2e^-) + \frac{1}{2}O_2 + H_2O \rightarrow \text{Cathode} + 2OH^-$$

In the absence of an electrical connection between the anode and cathode, these reactions quickly achieve equilibrium. The ideal cell voltage ("open

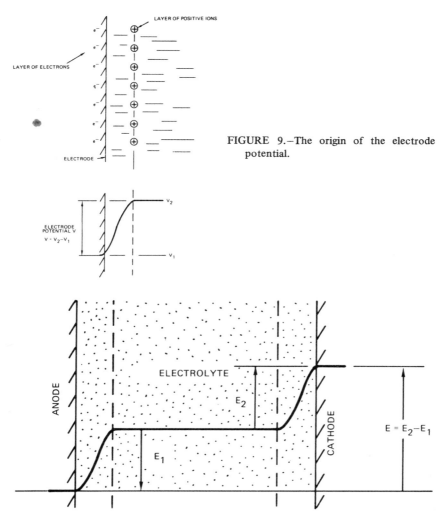

FIGURE 9.—The origin of the electrode potential.

FIGURE 10.—Cell potential as sum of half-cell voltages.

circuit" voltage) is equal to the potential E, and no further fuel or oxidizer is consumed.

The cell maintains this voltage because the electrons cannot travel through the electrolyte, since it is not a good conductor. However, if a lamp or an electric motor is connected across the terminals of the cell, electrons will flow through it from anode to cathode under the influence of the fuel cell's voltage or potential. This flow of electrons, or current, can be made to do useful work (i.e., light a lamp or turn a motor).

As electrons are removed from the anode, hydroxyl ions combine with hydrogen ions to form water. As the adsorbed hydrogen is consumed in this way, fresh gas from the supply diffuses through the electrode to take its place. At the cathode, returning electrons facilitate the production of hydroxyl ions from the oxygen and from water in the electrolyte. The hydroxyl ions, which are free to move in the electrolyte, flow from cathode and anode, completing the electrical circuit. Although all the hydroxyl ions are consumed in the reaction, only half of the water formed at the anode is consumed in the cathodic reaction. The remaining water constitutes a byproduct of the reaction and must be removed to avoid diluting the electrolyte. These reactions are shown in figure 11.

The foregoing description is a simplification of the processes that take place within a practical fuel cell. Moreover, the reactions differ in detail between one type of cell and another since they depend upon the fuel-oxidizer-electrolyte combination in use, and to a lesser extent on the temperature and pressure at which the cell operates. Nevertheless, the description of the essential mechanisms of voltage origin and ionic transport in the hydrogen-oxygen-alkaline fuel cell serves to illustrate the general principles of operation, and this description will aid in examining the fuel cell as a power-generating device.

POWER GENERATION

The discussion of electrode reactions stated that the open circuit voltage of the fuel cell is equal to the sum of the electrode potentials, E. The potential difference or voltage generated within the cell when no current is being drawn (and therefore no useful work is being done) is determined by the free energy of reaction of the chemical constituents of the cell. For hydrogen and oxygen this is 1.23 volts at 10.13 N/cm^2 (1 atmosphere) and 25° C. (77° F.). The value of E varies from a few millivolts (nitrous oxide and chlorine) to almost 3 volts (hydrogen and fluorine) depending upon the electrochemical couple, but

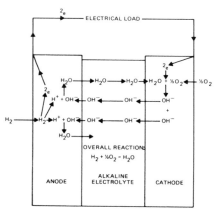

FIGURE 11.—Schematic representation of reactions taking place in a hydrogen-oxygen fuel cell with an alkaline electrolyte.

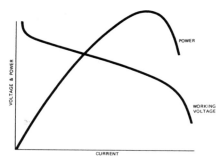

FIGURE 12.—Voltage, current and power relationships in a typical fuel cell.

Austin (ref. 6) has shown that for several preferred couples the open circuit potential lies in the range of 1.12 to 1.56 volts.

When current is drawn from the cell, however, the working voltage falls to a lower value as shown in figure 12. Because the power output of the cell is the product of the instantaneous voltage and current, it rises from zero (at zero current) to some maximum and then declines as increasing current drain causes greater and greater loss in voltage.

The loss in voltage that occurs when current is drawn from the cell is termed "polarization," and results from three major loss mechanisms. These losses are of paramount concern to the fuel cell designer since they result in decreased efficiency and power. Maximization of efficiency and power as a function of weight, volume, or cost is almost invariably a design goal.

To appreciate the design and construction features of fuel cells, it is advantageous to understand these loss mechanisms and the ways of reducing their effects.

LOSS MECHANISMS

The three basic loss mechanisms encountered in fuel cell operation are ohmic, concentration, and activation polarization. Ohmic polarization occurs as a result of electrical resistance losses in the cell. These resistances occur in the electrolyte, in the electrodes and, to a lesser extent, in the terminal connections of the cell. Because the fuel cell is an inherently low voltage device, significant currents must be drawn to generate useful amounts of power. Since ohmic (IR) losses are directly related to current, even quite small resistances can give rise to significant losses. For example, in a cell producing 200 amperes at approximately 0.55 volt, an internal resistance of only 1/1000 of an ohm causes an ohmic polarization loss of 0.2 volt. This represents a loss of approximately 36 percent in power output at peak power. To reduce such losses, electrodes are designed to have high conductivity and are closely spaced to minimize electrolyte resistance.

The second type of loss, concentration polarization, is caused by electrolyte depletion in the region of the electrode-electrolyte interface. Since the reactions producing the flow of current cannot take place in the absence of reactants and their intermediate products (e.g., hydroxyl ions), any reduction in availability of these supplies leads to a corresponding loss in output of the cell. Cells are therefore constructed so that reactants may be fed to as large an area of the electrode as possible, and electrodes are made highly porous to minimize mass transport losses. Electrolytes are used at high concentrations to ensure an adequate supply of ions at the electrodes.

The last type of loss, activation polarization, results when the interaction of an oxidant or fuel with its electrode is too slow. When this happens, a portion of the electrode potential is lost in driving the reaction to the rate required by the current demand. The reaction rate is dependent upon the activity or energy state of the molecules participating in the reaction, and it increases with temperature. Therefore, activation polarization may be reduced by raising the operating temperature of the cell or by increasing the activity through the use of a catalyst.

CHAPTER 4

Theory into Practice

After reviewing the fuel cell's operational principles and the mechanisms that limit performance, it is appropriate to consider the construction of a practical hydrogen-oxygen fuel cell and its integration into a system or powerplant. The last chapter concluded with some general guidelines for reducing the polarization, or voltage loss, in a fuel cell operating under load. These guidelines will be examined to show how they effectively dictate the geometry or layout of single cells and thus, to an extent, the design of fuel cell systems.

THE DESIGN PROCESS

In most engineering endeavors it is unusual to find an unmitigated solution to a given problem. Most frequently the solution to one problem gives rise to another, so that the procedure becomes one of compromise, selecting a solution that approaches the design goal as closely as possible without creating more problems than it solves. So it is with the fuel cell. Moreover, each type of fuel cell possesses its own set of problems and solutions, making it difficult to formulate a completely general description of the design process. Therefore, for the purposes of illustration we shall look first in a general way at fuel cell design, and then at some specific examples to see how this design procedure has been implemented.

A PRACTICAL FUEL CELL

The representation of a fuel cell in figure 1 embodies the essential elements of a single cell, but if such a cell were constructed it would perform poorly for a number of reasons. The reactants would have to travel considerable distances through the porous electrodes to reach the extremities, and under high current demand the lower ends of the electrodes would probably be "starved" of gas. The hydroxyl ions flowing from anode to cathode would have to traverse a wide gulf of electrolyte and the cell would suffer ohmic losses as a result. Another obstacle encountered with such a cell would be that of building a "stack" or battery of cells to attain an acceptable system voltage; the result would be far from compact, to say the least.

Many of these problems had been addressed and solved, at least partially, in Bacon's cell and devices built by others at that time. The solution was to construct cells in a thin sandwich or wafer configuration as shown in figure 13. Consider for a moment the behavior of a single cell of this kind. Each electrode

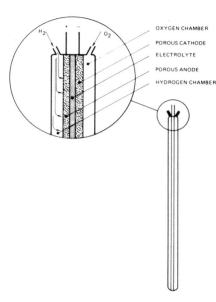

OXYGEN CHAMBER

POROUS CATHODE

ELECTROLYTE

POROUS ANODE

HYDROGEN CHAMBER

FIGURE 13.—Sandwich configuration of a
practical fuel cell.

is backed by a plenum or gas chamber so that the reactants are supplied
uniformly and with minimum loss to the total surface of the electrode. The
structure is thin, minimizing mass transport losses and pressure drops across the
electrode. The electrolyte is retained between the electrodes so only a thin
layer separates them, reducing ionic transport losses and ohmic resistance in
the electrolyte. The electrodes are good conductors (or are intimately bonded
to a conducting screen), so the ohmic losses in the electron flow circuit are
kept to a minimum. By virtue of the wafer-like shape of the cell, numbers of
cells may be stacked efficiently in a small space as shown in figure 14,
permitting the assembly of a compact stack of cells each capable of producing
relatively large quantities of power.

It is evident that this configuration has a number of advantages, but its use
also presents some problems. Difficulties are encountered in retaining the
electrolyte due to the thinness of the electrodes, and making thin electrodes of
sufficient strength and rigidity may be a problem. The close spacing of the cells
restricts access to the electrodes so that the supply of reactants and the
removal of electricity, heat, and product water becomes complicated as
evidenced in figure 15. In addition, the complete fuel cell system may need
pressure and flow regulators, pumps and motors to supply or circulate
reactants and coolants, and radiators or condensors to reject waste heat and
water. Electrical circuit protection, switching and power conditioning equipment may also be required. A practical fuel cell system may, therefore, be
quite complex as evidenced by the block diagram in figure 16.

The following paragraphs briefly outline some of the techniques used in cell

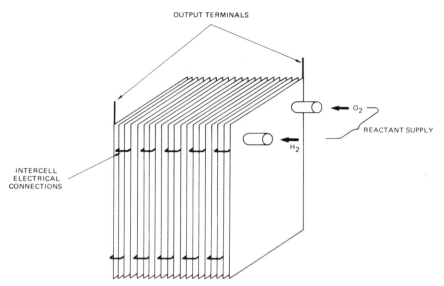

FIGURE 14.—Individual fuel cells assembled into a compact stack or fuel battery.

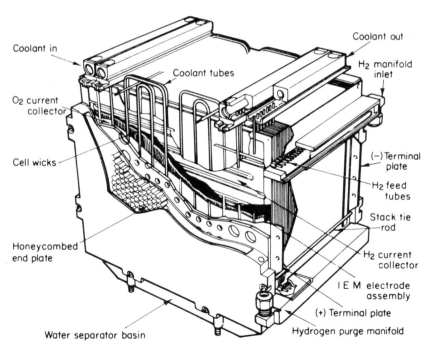

FIGURE 15.—Piping and wiring complexity of multicell stack illustrated in cutaway of a 350-watt Gemini fuel cell module.

FUEL CELLS

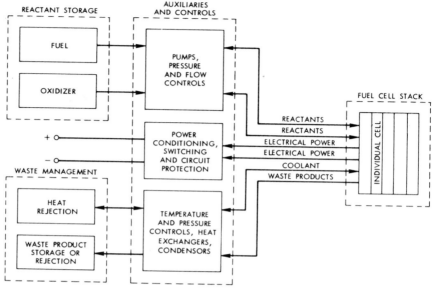

FIGURE 16.—Block diagram of a typical fuel cell system.

and stack construction of low and medium temperature hydrogen-oxygen fuel cells.

Reactant Feed Systems

Gaseous fuel and oxidizer may be fed to the cell in several ways as shown in figure 17. These may be described as dead-ended, circulating, and flow-through modes.

In the dead-ended supply mode the reactant is fed from a pressure vessel to the electrode gas chamber as in figure 17a. This system, which was used on the Gemini fuel cell, has the advantage of relative simplicity but does not provide for the removal of heat or product water from the cell, and impurities in the reactant may build up in the cell and block the electrode pores. Under fluctuating power requirements the cell output may vary because the system cannot adequately adjust the fuel supply to match the demand.

The circulating mode (fig. 17b) is more complex, requiring both inlet and exhaust ports for each cell and pumps to circulate the reactants. However, in this mode the reactants may be used to remove heat and/or water from the cell, and it is easier to match the fuel supply to the demand. The circulating reactant mode is used on the Apollo spacecraft fuel cell system.

The flow-through mode depicted in figure 17c combines some of the advantages of the former two modes at the expense of fuel economy. No circulating pumps or plumbing are required, and fluctuations in fuel demand

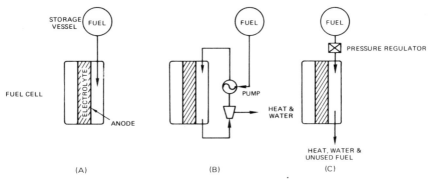

FIGURE 17.–Gaseous fuel-feed techniques. (A) Dead-ended mode. (B) Circulating mode. (C) Flow-through mode.

may be met reasonably well since there is always an excess of fuel in the supply stream. This mode was to be employed in a fuel cell designed for the Lunar Module, but batteries were eventually used instead. The technique is of interest only when the requirements for compactness and light weight override considerations of fuel economy. This system is employed in the oxidizer supply for an automobile fuel cell described in chapter 7. Air is used as the oxidizer and is simply blown through the cell and exhausted into the atmosphere; only the hydrogen fuel is supplied in a circulating mode.

When liquid reactants are used, or when gaseous reactants such as hydrazine are dissolved in the electrolyte, the feed system may be quite different from those described above.

Electrode Construction

The porous electrode, used in conventional hydrogen-oxygen fuel cells, has three basic functions:

(1) It must provide a large number of reaction sites of suitable activity where the gases and electrolyte can react.

(2) It must maintain the interface between the electrolyte and the gases so that electrolyte does not leak into the gas chamber and gas does not bubble into the electrolyte.

(3) It must provide a conductive path for the flow of electrons to and from the reaction site.

The development of electrodes to meet these conflicting demands undoubtedly has made the most significant single contribution to improvement in fuel cell performance.

Several techniques have been developed for constructing suitable porous electrodes. One of the earliest was the porous nickel electrode employed by Bacon in his pioneering fuel cell and since used in the Apollo fuel cell system.

Bacon produced his biporous electrodes by making a mixture of nickel powder and ammonium bicarbonate, compacting the mixture into a flat plaque, and firing the plaque in a furnace in a reducing atmosphere. This process sintered the nickel together and evaporated the ammonium bicarbonate, leaving a highly porous structure. Additional nickel powder was then sintered onto one surface to make a fine-pore layer.

This type of electrode relies on the activity of the nickel at elevated temperature to provide the necessary catalytic action. The electrolyte is retained by virtue of the dual porosity of the electrode and a small pressure differential. The capillary forces that draw the electrolyte into the fine-pore layer are sharply reduced at the boundary of the coarse-pore layer, so that raising the gas pressure slightly above that of the electrolyte maintains the gas/electrolyte interface close to this boundary.

Carbon and carbon-metal electrodes have been used successfully, notably by Union Carbide Corporation (ref. 7). Electrodes are made by mixing finely divided carbon (e.g., lampblack) with a binder and pressing the mix into the required shape; baking them removes some of the binder and results in a porous structure. Since carbon is not sufficiently active by itself, noble metal catalysts are incorporated during the manufacturing process. To retain the electrolyte, the carbon electrode must be wetproofed. Early electrodes made entirely of carbon were wetproofed by dipping them in wax. More recently, improved electrodes are formed on a porous nickel substrate and wetproofed by incorporating hydrophobic (water-repellant) materials such as polyethylene or PTFE* into the carbon layer. Careful grading of the wetproofing agents results in controlled localization of the reaction (wet/dry boundary) zone. One important advantage of this technique is that it allows the catalyst to be restricted to the reaction site instead of being spread through the electrode in a "shot gun" approach, permitting considerable savings in cost. Electrodes made in this manner, however, are quite complex, exhibiting as many as seven distinct layers and requiring many steps for their production.

Another type of porous electrode developed by American Cyanamid Corporation (ref. 8) has been used in a number of fuel cells with success. A mixture of catalyst such as platinum black is mixed with PTFE and rolled onto a fine nickel mesh or screen. The mixture is then pressed at high temperature to sinter the PTFE, forming a porous, catalytic plate bonded to the nickel screen. The PTFE effectively wetproofs the electrode, and the screen serves as both mechanical support and current collector.

In fuel cells other than those using hydrogen and oxygen the fuel is sometimes supplied as a gas dissolved in, or a liquid mixed with, the electrolyte. In these cases, the electrode need not be porous since fuel and electrolyte are both present at one face of the electrode. This may greatly

---

*PTFE, or polytetrafluoroethylene, is commonly known by brand names such as Teflon, etc.

simplify the electrode construction, reducing both the cost and the volume of the cell. For example, a very thin, ribbed metal sheet may be used with the catalyst simply applied to one surface.

Electrolyte Containment

The problem of preventing leakage of liquid or molten electrolyte through the porous electrodes used with gaseous fuels has already been discussed under Electrode Construction. Techniques relying on static pressure and capillary forces in the electrode were described.

An alternate technique first described by Mond and Langer, and currently employed, relies on the use of a matrix that soaks up the electrolyte like a sponge. The matrix consists of a fibrous separator between the electrodes; its capillary forces may be used alone or in conjunction with electrode wetproofing to retain the electrolyte. Mond and Langer recommended gypsum, cardboard or asbestos. Early fuel cells by Allis-Chalmers and more recent designs by Pratt & Whitney employed asbestos as a matrix material; other substances, such as potassium hexatitanate, are currently being studied.

The leakage of electrolyte may be reduced effectively if the electrolyte is solid at the cell's operating temperature. Such a design was General Electric's fuel cell for the Gemini spacecraft, which used a special plastic film in place of the more conventional type of electrolyte. A problem remains, however, with this type of electrolyte in maintaining the correct water content; this problem is discussed later in this chapter. A very different type of solid electrolyte has been used in high temperature fuel cells where certain ceramic materials have been found to exhibit ionic conductivity at a temperature of $1000°$ C. ($1832°$ F.), but problems associated with this high temperature have prevented extensive development of this type of cell.

Fuel cells using liquid fuels dissolved in the electrolyte may avoid the leakage problem by employing solid (nonporous) electrodes. However, as these types of cells are not hydrogen-oxygen cells, they are dealt with in chapter 5.

Heat and Water Removal

Fuel cells produce waste products in the form of byproducts of the chemical reaction and heat. The designer must provide for the removal of these products if the cell is to operate for more than a few minutes.

In the simplest form of heat removal (or thermal control) the fuel cell relies on purely passive techniques, conducting the heat away from the electrodes through their frames to the exterior of the cell where it is radiated. As fuel cells grow in power and are packed into smaller and smaller volumes, this passive technique becomes inadequate and designers have used an active system in which a coolant is passed through the cell. A technique employed by Pratt & Whitney in the Apollo fuel cell design uses the hydrogen fuel as a coolant, the hydrogen being circulated through the cell stack and then through a cooler. This method cannot be used, however, if the fuel is supplied in the dead-ended mode instead of being circulated. This was the case in the Gemini fuel cell and a separate coolant system had to be provided as a result. A third technique employed in nonaerospace fuel cells uses the electrolyte as a coolant. In fuel cells designed to operate for long periods of time, and subject to wide variations in load demand, it is advantageous to circulate the electrolyte so that its concentration may be maintained within prescribed limits. Such is the case with a hydrogen-air fuel cell designed by Union Carbide. In this system the electrolyte is passed through a heat exchanger and serves as the coolant.

The byproduct of the reaction in a hydrogen-oxygen cell is water, and this too must be removed if the cell is not to be flooded or the electrolyte diluted. Its removal poses only minor problems if the hydrogen fuel is circulated through the cell, for the hydrogen carries the water (or steam, in intermediate temperature cells) away from the electrodes so that it may be removed in a condenser or other suitable separator. This technique is used in the Apollo fuel cell. When fuel is not circulated, as in the Gemini design, an independent method of water removal must be employed. General Electric used a system of wicks in close contact with the electrode (see fig. 29) to remove water in the Gemini cell; the method is described in greater detail later in this chapter. Other techniques employed include the use of water diffusion membranes working in conjunction with cell vapor pressure variations.

Stack Construction

Having selected appropriate methods for feeding reactants to each fuel cell, removing its byproducts, cooling it, and assuring its continued operation through retention of electrolyte, the designer must arrange for the assembly of many cells into a stack, or fuel battery. In doing this, he must provide for mechanical integrity and maintenance of pressure seals, electrical connection between the cells, and the routing of reactants from a common supply point to each cell.

Two basic configurations are illustrated in figure 18. A commonly used arrangement (fig. 18a) simply stacks the cells one upon the other so that the cathode of one cell contacts the anode of the next, and so on. This has the advantage of connecting the cells electrically in series (the most common arrangement) without any external wiring; however, a separator must be placed between the cells to prevent the hydrogen and oxygen supplied to the adjacent anode and cathode from mixing. The separator may be simply a thin sheet of conducting material that is impervious to the gases. In another arrangement (fig. 18b), alternate cells are reversed so that they lie anode to anode, cathode to cathode, and so on. In this configuration the cells may share common gas chambers as shown, which simplifies the reactant supply system. But, electrical connections must be made externally if the cells are connected in series.

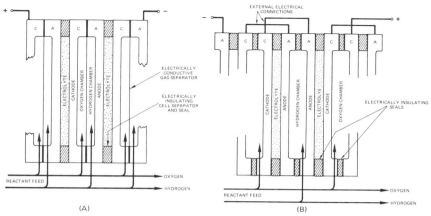

FIGURE 18.—Alternative cell-stacking techniques. (A) Sequential stack. (B) Back-to-back stack.

Low-pressure fuel cells may be pressure sealed by mounting the electrodes in a picture frame-shaped gasket and clamping the stack together, either by bolts passing through the gaskets or by an external clamping frame. Fuel cells designed by Union Carbide have been sealed by encapsulating the entire stack in an epoxy compound (see ch. 7).

In early fuel cells, such as those used on the Gemini and Apollo missions, reactants were fed to individual cells through small tubes (see figs. 15 and 23). Large numbers of these tubes then had to be connected to an external manifold, a time-consuming and expensive operation. Another approach is to build the supply manifolds into the electrode frames or separators. When the cells are stacked together the holes in the frame form a long continuous tube (or manifold) through the cell with small gas passages to the appropriate electrodes or gas chambers (fig. 19).

THE APOLLO FUEL CELL SYSTEM

When NASA selected the technology of Bacon's cell as the basis for the Apollo power-generation system, Pratt & Whitney Aircraft faced some severe development problems in qualifying the concept for manned spaceflight in a short period of time.

Bacon's observations had led him to operate his cell at a pressure of 414 N/cm^2 (600 psi). This high pressure required a very heavy mechanical structure to prevent leakage (see fig. 4), but high weight had to be avoided in designing a fuel cell for use in space. Initial tests on lightweight cells at Pratt & Whitney revealed severe leakage problems when the cell was operated at high pressure, and to alleviate them the pressure was lowered to approximately 34.4 N/cm^2 (50 psi). It may be remembered that the reason for raising the pressure in

28   FUEL CELLS

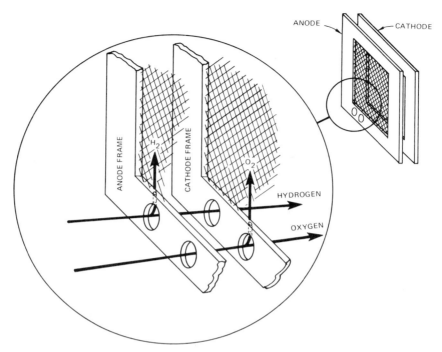

FIGURE 19.—Built-in reactant manifolds in electrode frames.

Bacon's cell in the first place to 138 N/cm^2 (200 psi) was to prevent the potassium hydroxide electrolyte from boiling at the 205° C. (400° F.) operating temperature. At 34.4 N/cm^2 (50 psi) this problem naturally reappeared. To circumvent the boiling problem Pratt & Whitney increased the concentration of the KOH solution from 30 percent to about 75 percent, which meant that at room temperature it was solid. To regain the performance lost by pressure reduction, the temperature was raised to 260° C. (500° F.). In bringing the cell up to temperature, the electrolyte changes from solid to molten, resulting in a complicated startup procedure taking several hours, and as long as 2 days are required to shut the cell down without damage. It was also necessary to build flexibility into the cell walls to accommodate changes in electrolyte volume due to variations in temperature and concentration.

The double-porosity layer electrodes also caused some difficulty during development. To maintain the gas/electrolyte interface at the boundary between the two pore sizes, the pressure differential between the gas and electrolyte required accurate control, resulting in a somewhat complicated system of sensors and valves. With the additional requirements for integration into an existing cooling system and the provision of potable water, the fuel cell system is far from simple (see fig. 24).

In practice, the long shutdown time does not affect the space flights (the fuel cells are jettisoned with the Apollo Service Module before reentry), and in use the system has worked faultlessly to achieve all its mission goals,* despite its complexity.

The Apollo fuel cell produces direct-current electrical power over a normal range of 563 to 1420 watts at a normal voltage range of 27 to 31 volts. The module (fig. 20) is 111.8 cm (44 in.) high by 57.2 cm (22.5 in.) in diameter and weighs approximately 111.1 kg (245 lb). Three of these modules, or powerplants, connected electrically in parallel, are used in the Apollo spacecraft to provide electrical power and potable water. The module is composed of four distinct sections or systems:

    (1) An energy-conversion section
    (2) A reactant-control system
    (3) A thermal-control and water-removal system
    (4) The necessary instrumentation

The last three systems are included in the accessory section.

---

*The explosion on the Apollo 13 mission occurred in the reactant supply system as a result of a prelaunch test malfunction, not in the fuel cell itself.

FIGURE 20.—Apollo 15-kW fuel cell powerplant.

The energy-conversion section comprises a stack of 31 Bacon-type, series-connected cells with associated gas manifolds and connecting leads. It is housed in a pressurized jacket which rests in an insulated support assembly. The components forming the accessory section are mounted on a Y-shaped frame atop the energy-conversion section. The accessory section consists of a nitrogen pressurization system; three regulators; a primary loop (hydrogen and water vapor); and a secondary loop (glycol and water); as well as heat exchangers, motor-driven pumps, and plumbing. A condenser connects the two fluid loops.

Before examining the system diagram, a discussion of single-cell operation is advantageous. Figure 21 shows the relative pressure differentials across the electrodes. The KOH-H_2O electrolyte solution is pressurized by a nitrogen blanket and regulated to 36.8 ± 0.69 N/cm^2 (53.5 ± 1.0 psi). The reactant regulators, using the nitrogen pressure as a reference, maintain differential pressures of 6.2 N/cm^2 (9.0 psi) for the hydrogen and oxygen above the nitrogen pressure. Two parameters governing the performance of the fuel cell system are the operating pressure of the system and the relative pressure differentials across the electrodes. The pressure differential across an electrode determines the location of the reactant/electrolyte interface. By extensive testing, the combination of pressure and pressure differentials shown in figure 21 has been found to be optimum for this system from the combined standpoints of performance and operational feasibility.

Figure 22 illustrates the construction of a single cell. The two electrodes within each cell are composed of dual-porosity sintered nickel which is formed from nickel powder pressed into sheets. The fine pores, approximately 50 microns (1 micron = 1/1000 mm) in diameter, are on the electrolyte side. The two electrodes are similar in construction, but the oxygen electrode has a coating of black, lithium-impregnated nickel oxide on the electrolyte side to inhibit oxidation. The electrode materials serve as catalysts in the electro-chemical reaction and are resistant to corrosion by the electrolyte. A pure nickel backup plate supports each electrode and also acts as a gas housing. A PTFE seal, which extends around the periphery of the cell, contains the electrolyte and is the electrical insulator. Although the electrodes are only about 21.6 cm (8-1/2 in.) in diameter, the entire cell is approximately 28.6 cm (11-1/4 in.) in diameter. Figure 23 shows a portion of a cell in section. The diaphragm section (between the electrodes and the cell spacer) accommodates changes in electrolyte concentration as the flexible backup plates expand and contract. The 31 cells are stacked in series and held together by torsion tie rods. Figure 24 is a schematic diagram of the system. Certain components not essential to this description are omitted. The diagram is coded to aid in distinguishing the different fluid paths.

The nitrogen subsystem is composed of a small nitrogen tank (which holds approximately 0.2 kg (0.5 lb) of nitrogen at 1035 N/cm^2 (1500 psi)), a

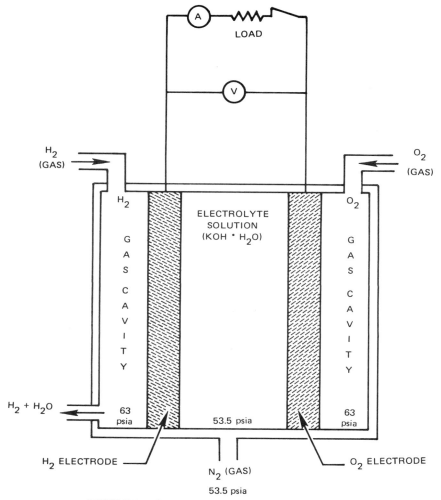

FIGURE 21.—Pressure differentials in an Apollo fuel cell.

nitrogen regulator, and connecting lines. The regulated nitrogen pressure 36.8 ± 0.69 N/cm^2 (53.5 ± 1.0 psi) serves a threefold purpose:

(1) It is used as a reference pressure for the hydrogen and oxygen regulators.

(2) It is used as a head pressure in the glycol accumulator.

(3) It pressurizes the jacket around the stack, thus pressurizing the electrolyte in each of the 31 single cells.

Hydrogen and oxygen are supplied to the powerplant from a cryogenic storage system. Hydrogen is stored at a nominal 169 N/cm^2 (245 psi) and

FUEL CELLS

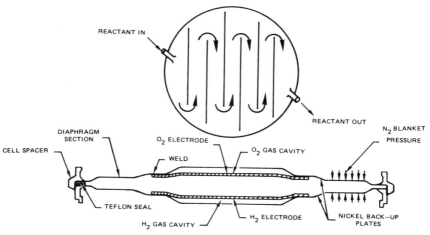

FIGURE 22.—Apollo fuel cell construction.

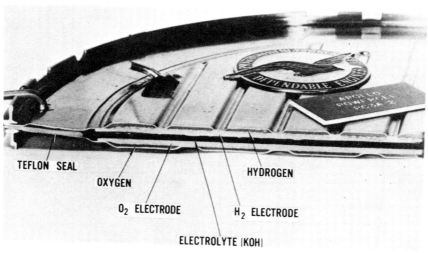

FIGURE 23.—Section through an Apollo free-electrolyte fuel cell.

oxygen at a nominal 621 N/cm² (900 psi). The gases are warmed by flowing through the connecting lines between the cryogenic storage system and the fuel cell system. Then, the gases enter the reactant preheaters before being regulated to normal operating pressures. The hydrogen and oxygen subsystems are each equipped with purge valves which, when electrically energized, permit a continuous flow of additional reactant through the cells. The surplus is dumped overboard. The purging process is repeated at regular intervals to remove impurities carried into the cells by the reactants.

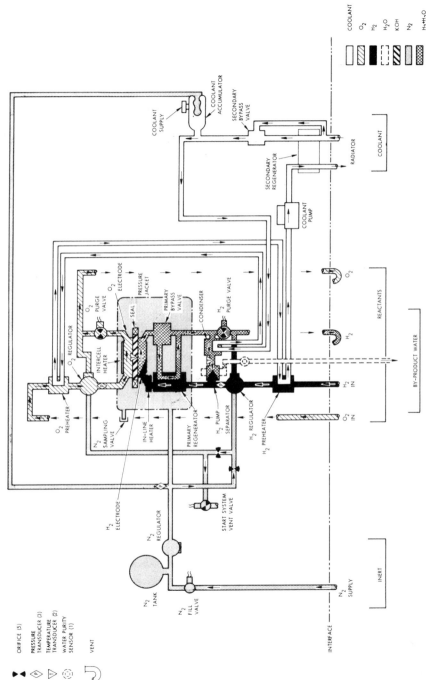

FIGURE 24. – Apollo fuel cell powerplant flow schematic (Model PC3A-2 Block II).

The makeup (or consumption) hydrogen enters the primary loop at the pump-separator exit. There it mixes with the recirculating hydrogen and water vapor and proceeds into the pressure jacket through the primary regenerator, where the mixture is heated, and from there into the stack. The primary (or hydrogen) loop consists of the primary regenerator and bypass control, the hydrogen pump-separator-motor assembly, a condenser, and an inline heater for temperature control under low-power conditions.

The primary bypass valve sensor detects stack exhaust temperature, which is essentially equal to stack temperature. The sensor is a bimetallic strip that acts as a flow diverter. Under high-power conditions when a large amount of heat must be rejected, the stack temperature is high and the bypass valve is open (this is a proportional-control valve). Under low-power conditions when heat must be conserved, the bypass valve is closed, permitting maximum regeneration.

The pump-separator is a positive-displacement unit. It circulates the hydrogen and water vapor mixture through the cells to remove waste heat and product water. Liquid water from the condenser is separated from the gas stream by centrifugal action. Input power to the motor (approximately 85 watts) is supplied by three-phase, 400-cycle, 115-volt spacecraft inverters.

FIGURE 25.—Gemini 1-kW fuel cell powerplant.

The condenser serves a twofold purpose. First, it maintains the primary loop heat balance by rejecting waste heat to the glycol loop for transfer to the radiators. Second, it maintains the mass balance in the primary loop by condensing the product water vapor from the cells before this water is removed by the separator.

The secondary loop uses a coolant mixture of ethylene glycol and water. The loop consists of a glycol pump, the condenser and preheaters previously discussed, a coolant accumulator, and a secondary regenerator and bypass valve. The positive-displacement glycol pump circulates the coolant through the secondary loop components and the radiator system. Power for the pump (approximately 25 watts) is provided by the same spacecraft inverters that supply the hydrogen pump. The coolant accumulator maintains a constant pressure within the coolant system regardless of volumetric changes caused by coolant temperature variations.

The secondary regenerator controls the heat transferred from the power-plant to the spacecraft heat rejection system to provide the condenser with a relatively constant coolant inlet temperature. The secondary bypass valve, which is controlled by the condenser exit temperature on the primary side, modulates the glycol flow through the cold side of the secondary regenerator. As the primary-side condenser exit increases, more of the glycol flow bypasses the secondary regenerator. Less of the glycol flow bypasses the secondary regenerator as the temperature decreases.

THE GEMINI FUEL CELL SYSTEM

General Electric's work on a fuel cell system for the NASA Gemini program began at about the same time as that on the Apollo system. However, the technology selected as the basis for the Gemini fuel cell differed significantly from the high temperature, high-pressure approach of Bacon. It was based on a solid electrolyte concept proposed by Grubb (ref. 9) in 1957 and represented a later technology than Bacon's, even though Gemini flew several years before Apollo.

The solid polymer electrolyte, or ion-exchange membrane (IEM) as it came to be known, consists of a lacy organic structure to which charged groups are firmly bonded. Ions of the opposite charge are loosely bonded to the polymer chains and are mobile within the membrane, providing the required ionic transport mechanism. Electrolyte containment problems are obviated since the membrane has well-defined boundaries. Membranes may be made cationic (i.e., having mobile cations such as H^+) or anionic (e.g., mobile OH^-). The Gemini fuel cell used a cationic membrane of sulphonated polystyrene.

The advantage of electrolyte immobility was offset somewhat by the ohmic resistance of the membrane, which was higher than that of a conventional electrolyte of equivalent thickness. However, it was possible to make the IEM extremely thin and thereby regain much of the lost performance. A persistent problem encountered by the engineers at General Electric Company's Direct Energy Conversion Operation was that of maintaining the correct water balance in the cell. Because the water generated in the cathode reaction could not be absorbed in the membrane it tended to flood the electrode so that positive water removal was essential. However, the membrane was damaged if allowed to dry out, so that a very careful balancing of the membrane water content was required. This was achieved by the use of fibrous transport channels, or wicks, carrying the excess water to a ceramic porous separator. Here the water was separated from the oxygen and routed to an accumulator for storage.

The Gemini fuel cell system was used successfully on seven manned flights.

FIGURE 26.—350-watt Gemini fuel cell stack.

The average power produced by the systems was 620 W and a total operating time of 840 hr was logged.

The power system consisted of two sections, plus an associated reactant supply system. Each section was approximately 66 cm (25 in.) long and 33 cm (12.5 in.) in diameter, and weighed approximately 31 kg (68 lb) including accessories (fig. 25). The section contained three stacks of 32 cells and produced 1 kw at 23.3 to 26.5 V. The system was flexible in operation. Each stack or section (fig. 26) could be removed from the bus at any time and could be replaced on the bus after extended periods of open circuit.

Two stacks were required for powered-down flight (17 A), and five stacks were needed for maximum loads. To provide electrical power, each cell had to interface with the hydrogen and oxygen supply system and with the water system (fig. 27).

Oxygen and hydrogen reactants for the fuel cell were stored in a supercritical cryogenic state in tanks located in the spacecraft adapter section. Each tank contained heaters for maintaining the oxygen operating pressure between 544 and 618 N/cm^2 (800 and 910 psi) and hydrogen pressure between 143 and 170 N/cm^2 (210 and 250 psi). Relief valves prevented pressures in excess of 690 N/cm^2 (1000 psi) for oxygen and 238 N/cm^2 (350 psi) for hydrogen.

Between the storage tanks and the main control valves, the reactants passed through heat exchangers that increased the temperature of the reactants to near fuel cell temperatures, thus preventing a thermal shock on the cell. Temperatures in the heat exchangers were controlled by the primary and secondary coolant loops.

Dual pressure regulators supplied hydrogen at a nominal 1 N/cm^2 (1.7 psi) above water pressure and oxygen at 0.3 N/cm^2 (0.5 psi) above hydrogen pressure. One regulator was provided for each section, with a crossover network that enabled one of the regulators to supply both sections if the other regulator failed. Separate control valves provided gaseous hydrogen to each stack. Each stack was provided with a hydrogen purge valve and an oxygen purge valve for removing accumulated impurity gases. A water valve and separate hydrogen and oxygen valves upstream of the regulators were provided in case a section had to be shut down.

The smallest active element of the fuel cell section was the thin, individual fuel cell which was 20-cm long and 18-cm wide (8 x 7 in.). Each cell consisted of an electrolyte-electrode assembly with associated components for gas distribution, electrical current collection, heat removal, and water control.

The metallic-catalytic electrode structure of the fuel cell contained an anode and a cathode which were in contact with a thin, solid plastic electrolyte, or ion-exchange membrane, to stimulate the exchange of hydrogen ions between electrodes (fig. 28). In the presence of the metallic catalyst, hydrogen gave up electrons to the electrical load, and released hydrogen ions which migrated through the electrolyte to the cathode. At the cathode, the ions combined with

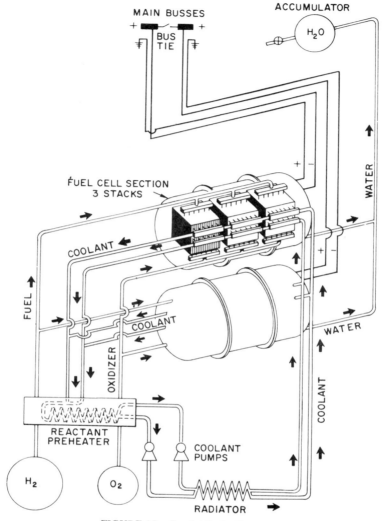

FIGURE 27.–Gemini fuel cell system.

oxygen and electrons from the load circuit to produce water that was carried off by wicks to a collection point. Ribbed metal current carriers were in contact with both sides of the electrodes to conduct the produced electricity.

Water formed in each cell during the conversion of electricity was absorbed by wicks (fig. 29) and transferred to a felt pad located on a porcelain gas-water separator at the bottom of each stack. Removal of the water through the separator was accomplished by the differential pressure between oxygen and water across the separator. If this differential pressure became too high or too

FIGURE 28.—Gemini single-cell assembly showing cathode side.

low, a warning light on the cabin instrument panel provided an indication to the flight crew. The telemetry system also transmitted this information to the ground stations. A similar warning system was provided for the oxygen-to-hydrogen gas differential pressure so that the appropriate action could be taken if out-of-specification conditions occurred.

The water produced by the fuel cell system exerted pressure on the PTFE bladders in water tanks A and B. Water tank A also contained drinking water for the flight crew, and the drinking water pressure resulted from the differential between the fuel cell product-water pressure and cabin pressure. Tank B was precharged with a gas to 13.1 N/cm² (19 psi), and the fuel cell product water interfaced with this gas. However, the pressure changed with drinking water consumption, fuel cell water production, and temperature. If the pressure exceeded 14 N/cm² (20 psi), the overpressure was relieved by two regulators. This gas pressure provided a reference pressure to the two dual

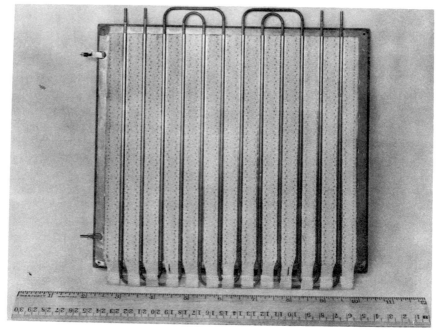

FIGURE 29.—Gemini cell assembly cooling and wick plate.

regulators that controlled the flow of the oxygen and hydrogen gases to the fuel cell sections.

The coolant system also interfaced with the fuel cell. The spacecraft had two coolant loops: the primary loop passed through one fuel cell section and the secondary loop through the second section. In each section the coolant was split into two parallel paths. For the coolant system, the stacks were in series and the cells were in parallel. Coolant-flow inlet temperature was regulated to a nominal 24° C. (75° F.).

CHAPTER 5

Down to Earth

INTRODUCTION

Up to this point we have considered only fuel cells that use hydrogen as fuel and pure oxygen as oxidizer. There are good reasons for selecting these reactants for spacecraft power supplies, but in terrestrial applications hydrogen and oxygen are presently far from ideal for a number of reasons. It is appropriate to pause and consider the implications of using fuels other than hydrogen.

A prime consideration of any item for space flight is its weight, particularly for lunar landing and return flights. A very small increase in the weight of the returnable payload results in an extremely large increase in the liftoff weight of the launch vehicle and a corresponding increase in total cost. This is amply illustrated by the Apollo system in which the 12 600-lb Command Module, the only portion which eventually returns safely to earth, is part of a gigantic 5-1/2-million lb launch vehicle/payload package at liftoff. Clearly, a component that offers a saving in weight, even though it may cost much more than a heavier alternative, can effect an overall reduction in mission cost.

Hydrogen and oxygen are capable of releasing more energy, pound for pound, than most alternate fuel-oxidizer combinations, and therefore offer a potentially lighter fuel cell. The disadvantage of their gaseous form, requiring large storage volumes, is not relevant to space missions on which they are customarily carried in liquid form at low temperatures. The reaction byproduct, water, is an advantage on manned spaceflights because it can provide drinking water for the astronauts.

However, none of these arguments is as compelling for a fuel cell used on earth, and the selection of an "ideal" fuel must be based on other criteria. Among these are such factors as the cost, availability, storability, volume, and transportability of the fuel. Priorities among these criteria depend upon the particular application; of more immediate concern at this point are the consequences of the selection on the performance, cost, and lifetime of the fuel cell.

FUELS OTHER THAN HYDROGEN

One method of classifying useful fuels has been suggested by Liebhafsky (ref. 10), in which he divides them into hydrogen, the hydrocarbons, and "compromise" fuels. Hydrogen is set in a class alone because of the simplicity with which it reacts, a characteristic probably responsible for its relatively high reactivity. The hydrocarbons, which as a class include the most common fuels such as gasoline, natural gas and kerosene, are far less reactive than hydrogen, much more difficult to oxidize, and may produce undesirable byproducts. This makes their use in fuel cells less attractive and the performance of such cells inferior to that of the hydrogen-oxygen cell. However, they are generally cheaper than hydrogen, much easier to handle, and readily available through existing distribution networks. Many believe that it is only through the use of hydrocarbons that the fuel cell will achieve widespread application in the public domain. The more common hydrocarbons are listed in table 1.

TABLE 1.—*Potential Fuels for Fuel Cells*

Some Hydrocarbons			
Methane	CH_4	Hexane	C_6H_{14}
Ethane	C_2H_6	Cyclohexane	C_6H_{12}
Ethylene	C_2H_4	Benzene	C_6H_6
Acetylene	C_2H_2	Heptane	C_7H_{16}
Propane	C_3H_8	Toluene	C_7H_{14}
Propylene	C_3H_6	Octane	C_8H_{18}
Butane	C_4H_{10}	Nonane	C_9H_{20}
Butene	C_4H_8	Decane	$C_{10}H_{22}$
Pentane	C_5H_{12}	Hexadecane	$C_{16}H_{34}$
		Kerosene (approx)	$C_{12}H_{26}$

Some Compromise Fuels	
Methanol (methyl alcohol)	CH_3OH
Ammonia	NH_3
Hydrazine	N_2H_4

The difficulties encountered with the hydrocarbons have prompted the investigation of compromise fuels. The reactivity of these fuels lies between that of hydrogen and the hydrocarbons, and they are generally easier to use. Hydrazine in particular exhibits some very desirable characteristics. It is highly reactive at normal temperatures and does not require expensive catalysts. It may be dissolved in an aqueous electrolyte as hydrazine hydrate, thereby simplifying the fuel cell system and permitting the use of nonporous electrodes, which offer savings in cost and volume over cells employing gas-diffusion electrodes (fig. 30). Unfortunately, the cost of hydrazine is 15 to 20 times that of hydrogen, making it by far the most expensive fuel used or proposed for use in fuel cells. In addition, it is poisonous and extreme care is required in handling it, a factor that presently precludes its use by the public. Despite these problems, hydrazine-powered fuel cells have been the been the subject of considerable development and have been used as small portable

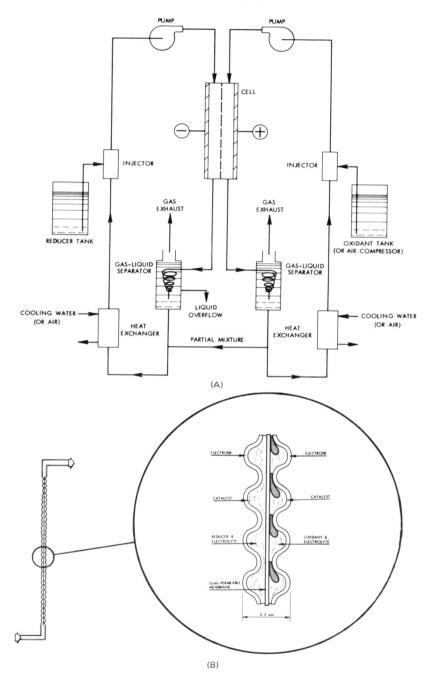

FIGURE 30.—A hydrazine-hydrogen peroxide fuel cell system. (A) Schematic of closed
electrolytic cell. (B) Diagram of thin-cell configuration.

supplies for military purposes (ref. 11) and power sources for submersible vehicles (ref. 12).

Like hydrazine, ammonia may be separated into hydrogen and nitrogen so that it does not suffer from the contamination problems inherent in carbonaceous fuels. Its cost is similar to that of hydrogen, but it is more readily available and easier to handle. Because of its solubility, it may be circulated in the electrolyte. Although its use is not without hazard, it is no more dangerous than gasoline. However, its reactivity is low and in practice it is preferable to dissociate the ammonia into hydrogen and nitrogen before it is fed to the anode (fig. 31), resulting in a fuel cell of increased complexity and reduced overall efficiency (ref. 13). Consequently, ammonia fuel cells have received little attention to date and are not considered suitable for economic power production except in specialized remote, low-power situations where the availability of ammonia makes it unusually attractive.

Fuel cells reacting methanol (methyl alcohol) have received more attention than ammonia cells, and a number of practical devices have been operated with some success (refs. 14, 15). Methanol costs about the same as hydrogen and its availability is high. It is liquid and can, therefore, be circulated in the electrolyte. However, methanol is less reactive than hydrogen and hydrazine, and oxidation produces carbon dioxide:

$$CH_3OH + H_2O \longrightarrow 6H^+ + 6e + CO_2$$

This implies limited usefulness of alkaline electrolytes such as aqueous KOH, because the CO_2 forms carbonates and bicarbonates that essentially inactivate the electrolyte in time. It must be renewed periodically, if used. Neutral solutions are poorly ionized and are not good conductors; acidic electrolytes such as sulfuric acid or phosphoric acid are therefore widely used. Materials that can be employed in the cell are restricted to those that can withstand the acid's corrosive effects. Additional problems are encountered due to the presence of the alcohol, which degrades the air electrode and coats platinum catalysts with products of partial alcohol oxidation. This catalyst "poisoning," as it is known, has been overcome by the development of less susceptible catalysts, and methanol-air fuel cells are currently under development by a joint French-American enterprise (see ch. 6).

HYDROCARBON FUELS

When a hydrocarbon is burned, oxides of carbon are produced. If a hydrocarbon fuel is reacted in a fuel cell, an acid electrolyte is used to avoid the carbonate problems discussed previously. This is not completely disadvantageous, because most hydrocarbon oxidation reactions favor the use of an acid electrolyte. However, the problems of materials compatibility and relatively poor cathodic (air-electrode) reaction must still be faced.

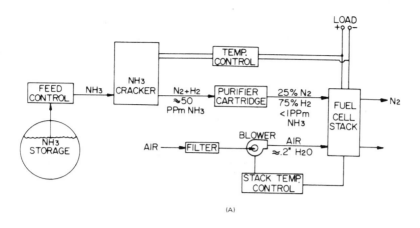

(A)

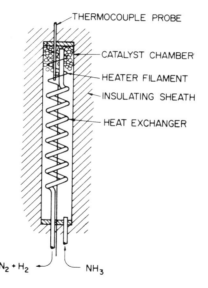

(B)

FIGURE 31.—Ammonia-air fuel cell system. (A) System flow schematic. (B) Ammonia cracker.

The difficulties of using hydrocarbon fuels do not end here. To make the oxidation reaction proceed at acceptable rates, large amounts of expensive catalysts and/or high temperatures must be employed. Clearly, an economic fuel cell cannot be built if it incorporates catalysts costing thousands of dollars for every kilowatt of power produced. On the other hand, high operating temperatures complicate the design of the fuel cell due to materials and construction difficulties, and may lead to unacceptably long startup times and operational hazards. In addition, at high temperatures carbon and other undesirable products may be deposited in the cell, further degrading its performance.

The difficulties of oxidizing hydrocarbons directly in a fuel cell have led to several concepts for converting the fuel into hydrogen outside the cell. These concepts give rise to a number of different fuel cell types.

TYPES OF HYDROCARBON FUEL CELLS

It is customary to classify fuel cells by their operating temperatures. However, for the purposes of this survey it is more helpful to differentiate between hydrocarbon cells by the manner in which the fuel is processed prior to or during oxidation. Three classes of cells are represented in figure 32.

The direct oxidation fuel cell works like the hydrogen-oxygen cell described in chapters 3 and 4, fuel being oxidized in the cell during the electrochemical reactions that produce electricity. Indirect oxidation cells use processed fuel that has been fully or partially oxidized before the electricity-producing stage. The processing of the fuel may take place outside the cell in a special processing unit (external oxidation) or adjacent to the anode in a special chamber that forms part of the fuel cell (internal processing).

Each of these cell types may be further subdivided according to the temperature of operation: low (up to 200° C., 400° F.), medium (200° to 500° C, 400° to 900° F.), and high (500° to 1000° C., 900° to 1800° F.).

DIRECT OXIDATION CELLS

Cells reacting hydrocarbon fuels directly at the anode with no intermediate processing must, because of their simplicity, be regarded as the ideal, general-purpose type. Several studies of this type of cell were made in the midsixties by Texas Instruments, the Institute of Gas Technology, General Electric Co., and others. The concepts that were examined embraced a wide range of temperatures and used aqueous (acid), molten carbonate, and solid

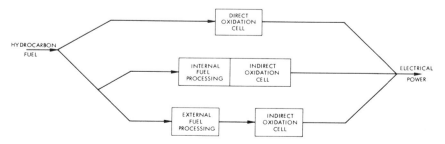

FIGURE 32.—Hydrocarbon-air fuel cell types.

zirconia electrolytes. The last concept, studied by Westinghouse, relies on the mobility of oxygen ions in ceramic zirconium oxide at very high temperatures (1000° C., 1800° F.). The zirconia is stabilized with oxides of thorium and cerium to retain its strength and refractory properties.

The design of a 500-watt system reacting propane and air was undertaken in 1966 by Onan Division of Studebaker Corporation (ref. 16). Operating at 204° C. (400° F.), the fuel cell stack used phosphoric acid in a porous PTFE matrix. Even at this medium temperature the cell required a heavy catalyst loading of platinum at the rate of 70 milligrams per square centimeter of electrode area. The system, shown in schematic form in figure 33, had a design life of about 500 hours. The cell's developers noted that the power output was increased "as much as tenfold" when water was added to the fuel. It is probable that this performance gain was due to the partial reforming of the fuel to hydrogen in the presence of steam at the anode. This is one of the techniques used in internal processing, indirect oxidation cells.

INDIRECT OXIDATION, INTERNAL PROCESSING CELLS

The difficulties inherent in the direct oxidation of hydrocarbons may be overcome to some extent by reforming the fuel at the anode to carbon monoxide and hydrogen as shown in figure 34. This type of cell operates above 500° C. (950° F.) and uses an electrolyte comprising molten carbonates of potassium, sodium, and lithium in a porous ceramic matrix. The cell is clearly not subject to carbonate contamination, since the electrolyte depends on

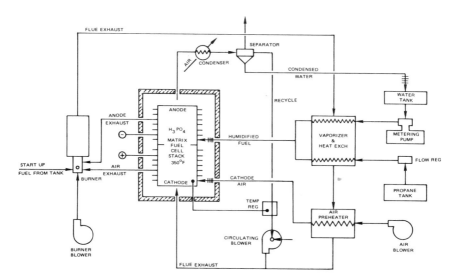

FIGURE 33.—Schematic of a direct oxidation propane-air fuel cell system.

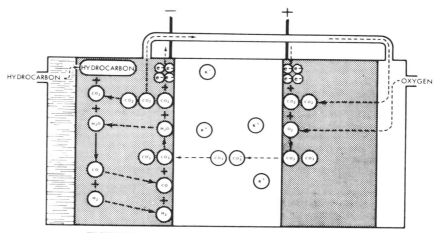

FIGURE 34.—Reactions in a molten carbonate fuel cell.

carbonates for its operation. Carbonates are replenished by recirculating CO_2 as shown or by the CO_2 in the air supply to the cathode. The cell operates without added catalysts because of the high operating temperature. Difficulties reported (ref. 17) with this type of cell include severe corrosion problems and high temperature chemistry limitations. Its performance with hydrocarbon fuels has not been good.

Another form of internal-reforming fuel cell relies on the use of a solid anode as a hydrogen-diffusion membrane. The fuel is reformed with steam in a catalytic chamber in contact with the palladium or silver-palladium anode. The anode allows only hydrogen to diffuse through to the electrolyte, which may be alkaline if carbon dioxide is removed from the air supply. Pratt & Whitney used the concept in 1964 (ref. 18) to react liquid hydrocarbons at a temperature of 260° C. (500° F.). More recently the internal-reforming fuel cell has been operated at temperatures in excess of 400° C. (750° F.) (ref. 19) using a palladium foil anode and nickel reforming catalyst. The anode consists of an oxide-coated nickel screen, and the electrolyte is a mixture of potassium and sodium hydroxides. The CO_2-free air is bubbled into the electrolyte between the screen and the cathode side of the container. This agitates the electrolyte and supplies fresh superoxide at the cathode to facilitate the reduction reaction. It is claimed that this cell shows good performance, but it has not yet been operated as a fuel battery or stack system. The cell has been developed jointly by divisions of Atlantic Richfield Co. and Bolt, Beranek, and Newman, Inc.

INDIRECT OXIDATION, EXTERNAL PROCESSING CELLS

The design of an indirect oxidation fuel cell may be simplified by processing the fuel outside the cell instead of at the anode. Three processes may be used in this type of cell: reforming, partial oxidation, and cracking.

In steam reforming the fuel is reacted with steam at high temperature (750° C., 1380° F.) and pressure to produce carbon monoxide and hydrogen. For methane, this is represented as:

$$CH_4 + H_2O + heat \rightarrow CO + 3H_2$$

In the presence of a catalyst (such as nickel or iron oxide), the carbon monoxide further reacts with the steam (the water-gas shift reaction) to form carbon dioxide and hydrogen:

$$CO + H_2O \rightarrow H_2 + CO_2$$

The carbon dioxide can be removed by passing the product gases through a scrubber of sodalime. Disadvantages of the system are the large amount of heat required and the sensitivity of the process to sulfur compounds in the fuel, which poison the reforming catalyst. The latter penalizes systems attempting to use liquid hydrocarbons, which are often heavily sulfurized, but does not significantly affect the use of low-sulfur gases. The method is used in demonstration devices built by Pratt & Whitney Aircraft in support of the TARGET consortium's Comprehensive Installation Program (see ch. 7). The carbon dioxide is not removed in this case, since the fuel cell uses phosphoric acid electrolyte and is not subject to carbonate formation.

Hydrocarbons may also be broken down by a partial oxidation process in which the fuel is incompletely burned with oxygen or air. The reaction products are hydrogen and carbon monoxide:

$$2CH_4 + O_2 \rightarrow 2CO + 2H_2$$

The use of pure oxygen for this process is clearly undesirable. However, when air is used the product gas contains only about one-third as much hydrogen by volume as that produced in the steam-reformer process (ref. 17). The method is not sensitive to sulfur in the fuel.

Certain fuels, such as ammonia, may be broken down into their component parts by thermal dissociation or cracking (see fig. 31). The process decomposes the fuel by heating it over an active catalyst. Thus, for ammonia:

$$2NH_3 + heat + catalyst \rightarrow N_2 + 3H_2$$

The technique is not readily applicable to complex hydrocarbons.

REGENERATIVE FUEL CELLS

One of the advantages of the fuel cell discussed in chapter 1 is its capability for continuous operation, giving it an operational life much greater than a comparable primary galvanic cell or battery. However, certain batteries can be recharged; that is, their reactants can be regenerated and used over and over again. This regeneration is usually performed electrically by driving a current through the cell in the reverse direction. Heat may also be used to perform this function in certain special "thermally regenerative" cells.

Fuel cells may also be made rechargeable, or regenerative, by passing a current in the reverse direction. In this mode the cell becomes, essentially, an electrolysis unit and in a sense predates the fuel cell. Of course, it is not possible to regenerate complex fuels in this manner but, fortunately, that is not generally desired.

A regenerative fuel cell of this kind could be beneficial to Earth-orbiting spacecraft (ref. 20) for two reasons. Most spacecraft use solar cells as a power source, but must rely on rechargeable (secondary) batteries to power them when in the shadow of the Earth. These batteries (usually banks of nickel-cadmium cells) are limited in the number of charge-discharge cycles that they can tolerate without deterioration, and are also limited in the amount of charge current that they can accommodate. Both of these factors lead to poor utilization of the true storage capacity of the batteries and result in heavy units. A regenerative fuel cell offers lighter weight because of the inherently higher energy potential of its reactants and because it is not limited in cycle life and charge rate to the same degree. Studies have shown that regenerative fuel cells may store four times as much energy for a given weight as secondary galvanic cells, and this is significant for communications satellites having high-power demands during the eclipsed portion of the orbit.

Regenerative fuel cells may also be advantageous in some terrestrial applications, but for different reasons. Because the reactants are reused, their cost becomes less significant so that reactants that are expensive when used continuously, such as hydrogen and oxygen, might find application where they are periodically regenerated from water. The high overall efficiency of the fuel cell is attractive in systems used to store electricity at "off peak" periods because the amount of electricity used to regenerate the reactants, and hence the cost of regeneration, is reduced. Such cells might therefore find application in large-scale storage systems at generating sites by smoothing the load demand variations.

The regenerative cell may be a single cell that is operated alternately in charge (electrolysis) and discharge modes (fig. 35). Alternatively, it may consist of individual power and electrolysis cells, either separate or integrated into a single unit as shown in figure 36. The former concept lends itself to simple mechanical arrangement, but is electrochemically difficult because the cell cannot be optimized for both charge and discharge modes. The integrated

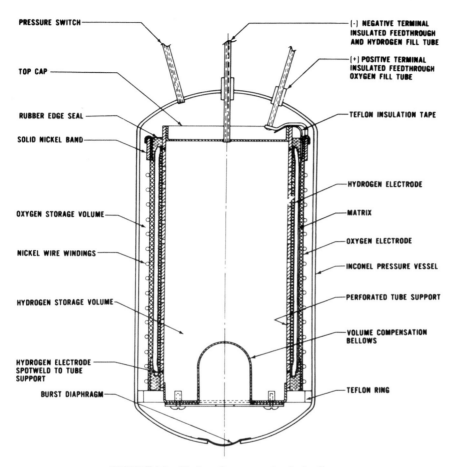

FIGURE 35.—Single-cell regenerative fuel cell.

dual-stack system can be well optimized for the charge-discharge cycle, but its construction poses some severe mechanical problems. This type of cell has been under development for some time by Pratt & Whitney. The single-cell concept was studied by Electro Optical Systems under contract to NASA, and is currently being investigated by Energy Research Corporation and Tyco Laboratories for the Communications Satellite Corporation. Tyco Laboratories also recently completed a study of rechargeable oxygen electrodes for NASA (ref. 21).

Low cost regenerative fuel cells operating at elevated pressure and temperature have been proposed (ref. 22). The concept uses nickel electrodes sintered into the inner and outer surfaces of a porous, calcia-stabilized zirconia cup, which serves both as a reactant-separation membrane and a structural

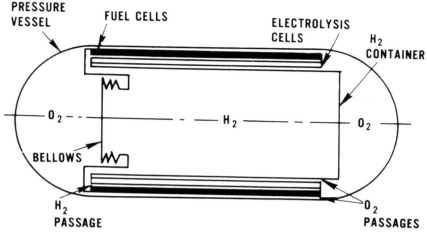

FIGURE 36.—Integrated dual-stack regenerative fuel cell concept.

member. Using aqueous potassium hydroxide electrolyte, the cell has been operated at pressures between 700 and 2000 N/cm^2 (1000 to 3000 psi) and temperatures of 150° to 175° C. (300° to 350° F.). The cell's developers concluded that the results obtained from several hundred hours of recycling indicated the feasibility of fabricating economic rechargeable fuel cells using no expensive materials. It was noted that the performance of the cell would have to be improved to make it economically attractive.

Fuel Cell Technology State-of-the-Art

INTRODUCTION

To summarize the state-of-the-art in a developing technology is never an easy task, for new developments are apt to make such a summary obsolete in a short time and rapid growth makes it difficult to ensure exhaustive coverage.

In reviewing fuel-cell terrestrial technology the problem is compounded. Much of the nonaerospace application work is concerned with the development of fuel cells for military applications, and as such is beyond the scope of this survey. A number of the remaining developmental efforts are aimed at competitive commerical markets; consequently data, particularly on performance and cost, are proprietary in nature and therefore not releasable.

Cost data in particular are difficult to establish for fuel cells because of the special-purpose nature of most of the applications to date. In general, cost has not been the predominant consideration in these applications, but rather the development and limited production of a device able to satisfy special constraints and requirements. Because only a few units have been built for each application, the devices must be regarded as prototypes, not production units, and are therefore high in cost.

Consequently, this chapter is a general guide to the present status of fuel cell technology for terrestrial applications. Detailed information on cost, performance, and lifetimes of various fuel cell types will become available as work currently in progress begins to yield data of this type.

At present, it is valuable to examine the state-of-the-art in fuel cells for aerospace applications because the time span covered by this work is sufficiently long to reveal significant improvements in the technology. It would be unwise to infer that advances of an equal magnitude can be expected in terrestrial fuel cell technology, because some of the aerospace cell advances have already been incorporated into their earthly counterparts; however, it is reasonable to assume that some reduction in cost and volume of future Earth-bound cells will be realized.

AEROSPACE FUEL CELLS

NASA is currently eyeing a fuel cell power supply for the space shuttle, a reusable vehicle that will ferry crew and supplies between Earth and orbiting spacecraft or platforms. The design goals for this system call for a 6 to 10-kW unit with a specific weight in the range of 4.5 to 13.5 kg/kW (10 to 30 lb/kW) and a design lifetime of 5000 to 10 000 hours. The reusable nature of the shuttle vehicle makes easy and rapid start/stop sequences of the fuel cell a prime requirement. Under contract to NASA's Manned Spacecraft Center in Houston, Texas, General Electric and Pratt & Whitney Aircraft are engaged in a technology demonstration program that will provide a baseline for the shuttle system design.

General Electric's approach uses a solid polymer electrolyte (ion-exchange membrane) of perfluorinated sulfonic acid with platinum black, metal screen electrodes. Thermal control is achieved by circulating coolant between adjacent anodes, and product water is removed from the wetproofed cathodes by capillary forces in a wick system similar to that employed in the Gemini fuel cell. The reactants are hydrogen and oxygen. Cells are constructed in a back-to-back configuration as in figure 37 to form a bi-cell assembly with a total active area of 650 cm^2 (0.7 ft^2). Components of a cell assembly are shown in figure 38.

The baseline system is rated at 5 kW and consists of 40 bi-cell assemblies in two stacks. Nominal operating temperature is 65° C. (150° F.), but it is claimed that the system will operate effectively over a wide temperature range. System output voltages of 28, 56, and 112 Vdc can be supplied by appropriate interconnection changes. System flexibility is considered by General Electric to be a major design feature. The baseline module weighs 68 kg (150 lb) and is packaged in a container of approximately 0.056 m^3 (6 ft^3) excluding controls. Figure 39 illustrates the system in schematic form.

Pratt & Whitney is also studying advanced shuttle fuel cell concepts under contract to NASA's Lewis Research Center, and has designed a cell capable of 7-kW sustained power that they estimate will weigh only 39 kg (85 lbs). A mock-up (nonworking model) of the proposed unit, shown in figure 40, measures 44 x 43 x 22 cm (17-1/2 x 17 x 8-1/2 in.) including controls, giving it a specific volume of 0.006 m^3/kW (0.209 ft^3/kW). The designers claim that this device could operate at a peak power level of 50 kW for short periods. A schematic of the proposed cell is shown in figure 41. This performance represents a current design goal and as such must be regarded as beyond the state-of-the-art.

Both shuttle system designs exhibit significant improvement in specific weight and volume over previous space fuel cell systems as summarized in table 2.

When the space shuttle and intermediate design programs are considered on the basis of improvement with time, dramatic advances in the technology are forecast, as illustrated in figure 42. Specific weight and volume should decrease by almost an order of magnitude (figs. 42a, 42b), while operating lifetime should increase to a similar degree (fig. 42c). During this period, per unit specific costs ($/kW) may fall to less than half their original value (fig. 42d).

As might be expected, these improvements are reflected in single cell

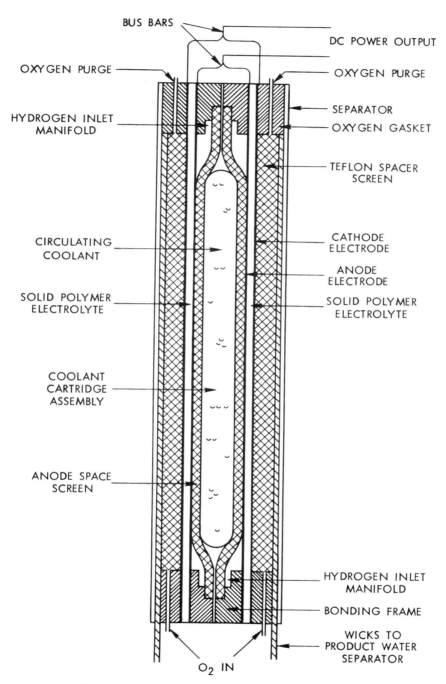

FIGURE 37.—Back-to-back fuel cell assembly schematic.

FIGURE 38.—Space shuttle fuel cell assembly.

performance also. A predominant characteristic in fuel cell performance is the current density that can be sustained without excessive polarization. For aerospace hydrogen-oxygen cell this has risen from between 31 and 125 mA/cm^2 (34 to 135 A/ft^2, (ASF)) to between 200 and 300 mA/cm^2 (216 and 324 ASF) under nominal operating conditions, with peak current densities as high as 1 to 2 A/cm^2 (1080 to 2160 ASF) being attainable for short durations. Specialized cells (ref. 23) have been operated at 2.7 A/cm^2 (2900 ASF), using open-cycle heat and product water removal. This technique results in high specific fuel consumption, but high-power density cells such as this might find application as emergency high-power backup power supplies as well as in missile and satellite systems.

NONAEROSPACE FUEL CELLS

In terms of development, the most advanced types of cells for terrestrial applications are those using hydrogen-air and hydrazine-air as reactants. Hydrogen-air cells developed directly from hydrogen-oxygen alkaline cells (ref. 24) have been used with a scrubber system to remove carbon dioxide from the air supply. The use of air limits the current density attainable in the cell to less than that achievable by an oxygen-breathing device for a given oxidizer flow rate, but practical cells have been operated at current densities better than 100 mA/cm^2 (108 ASF) using blower-supplied air (see ch. 7). Specific weights of 10 to 12 kg/kW (22 to 28 lb/kW) are state-of-the-art at specific volumes around 0.03 m^3/kW (1 ft^3/kW). Cells deriving hydrogen from metal hydrides have been built as portable low-power supplies (ref. 25). Hydrogen is stored in solid form as lithium hydride or sodium aluminum hydride and released by the addition of water to the hydride container. Both aqueous alkaline electrolyte and solid ion-exchange membranes have been used with this type of fuel to achieve system characteristics of 180 kg/kW (400 lb/kW) and 0.4 m^3/kW (14 ft^3/kW).

Fuel cells burning hydrazine with oxygen, hydrogen peroxide, or air have been taken to a fairly advanced stage of development and are currently being used by the U.S. Army as transportable power supplies in the low-power range of 50 to 500 watts (ref. 11), and have been used experimentally to power submersible vessels in the range of 750 to 2000 watts (ref. 12). Performance

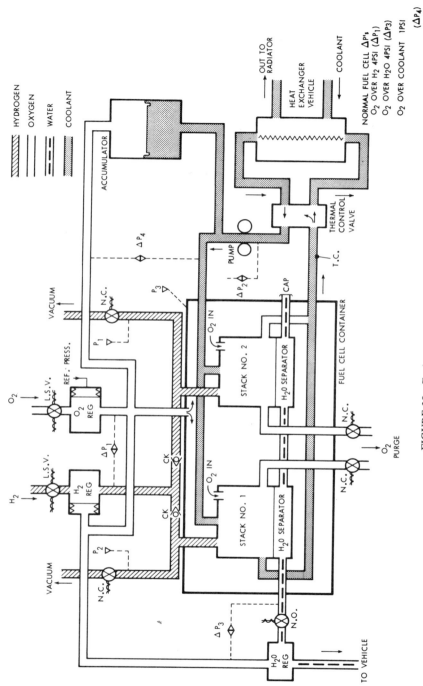

FIGURE 39.—Fuel cell module schematic.

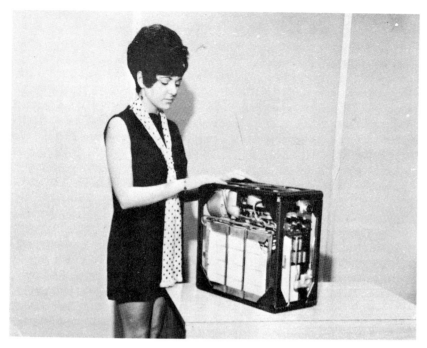

FIGURE 40.—Advanced 7-kW hydrogen-oxygen fuel cell powerplant.

parameters in the low-power range indicate specific weights of 60 kg/kW (130 lb/kW) and specific volumes of 0.1 to 0.15 m^3/kW (3.5 to 5.5 ft^3/kW). Estimates of cost (ref. 26) for systems of this type produced in quantities of 100 put the price per unit at about $30 000/kW, about an order of magnitude lower than aerospace hydrogen-oxygen cells of comparable power output.

The higher powered systems have been developed (ref. 12) by a French electrical equipment manufacturer, Alsthom, using a technique that offers significant potential reductions in manufacturing costs and results in very compact cell stacks. The nonporous electrodes consist of goffered (finely fluted) metal sheets a few tenths of a millimeter thick, separated by a semipermeable membrane (fig. 30). Hydrazine and hydrogen peroxide reactants dissolved in the electrolyte are circulated through the half-cells thus formed. The electrodes are made from 50μ sheets of nickel or stainless steel resulting in complete cells about 0.5-mm thick. Catalysts of cobalt or silver mixed with an adhesive resin are applied to the electrodes, which are then mounted in thin plastic frames. The method of assembly, illustrated in figure 43, permits the construction of very compact systems. Cell stacks of this type have achieved power densities of 0.001 m^3/kW (0.0035 ft^3/kW) at a specific weight of 2 kg/kW (4.4 lb/kW), and complete systems weigh 10 to 15 kg/kW with 4 kg/kW considered a feasible goal.

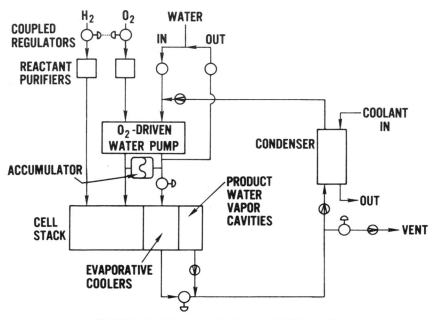

FIGURE 41.—Schematic of advanced 7-kW fuel cell.

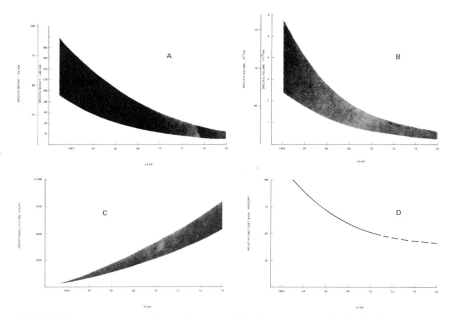

FIGURE 42.—Improvements in performance of hydrogen-oxygen fuel cells for aerospace applications, including projections.

TABLE 2.—*Aerospace Fuel Cell Performance Gains*

System	Apollo	Gemini	Space Shuttle
Power level (kW) (rated)	1.0	1.0	5
Specific weight, kg/kW (lb/kW)	115 (250)	30.8 (68)	13.6 (30)
Specific volume, m^3/kW (ft^3/kW)	0.167 (5.9)	0.051 (1.8)	0.034 (1.2)

Methanol-air fuel cells are also under development by Alsthom under a joint program with Esso Research and Engineering Company. The initial objective of the development program, which was begun in December 1970, is the development of a practical fuel cell system that would be competitive with small engine generators and batteries satisfying specialty and remote power requirements. The development of a fuel cell system for automotive propulsion could follow if the initial objective is achieved. Esso refuses to release information about the program on the grounds that all aspects are proprietary. Alsthom admits (ref. 12) that the use of methanol in the hydrazine-type cell structure still requires extensive fundamental work, particularly in connection with the development of cheap catalysts. Under the terms of the Alsthom-Esso agreement, Esso will contribute catalyst technology and conduct programs aimed at developing new and improved catalysts.

The most active development of hydrocarbon-burning cells is being undertaken by Pratt & Whitney for a consortium of gas and electric utility companies known as TARGET (see ch. 7). Developmental powerplants are currently undergoing field tests using methane and air as reactants. The methane is reformed externally with steam and the products are reacted in cells using phosphoric acid electrolyte.

An internal-reforming methane cell has been developed jointly by Bolt, Beranek, and Newman, Inc. and Atlantic Richfield Co. (ref. 19). Operating at $510°$ C. ($950°$ F.) and atmospheric pressure, the cell uses a molten alkaline electrolyte of sodium and potassium hydroxides. Methane (or, it is claimed, other hydrocarbon fuels) is reformed on a catalytic bed of nickel in a chamber adjacent to a palladium anode. Hydrogen formed in the chamber diffuses through the solid anode to react with the electrolyte. Air from which CO_2 has been removed is admitted to the cell on the cathode side. As it enters it agitates the electrolyte around the nickel screen cathode, forming a superoxide that facilitates the reduction process. Current densities as high as 600 mA/cm^2 (648 ASF) of anode area at 0.6 volt are claimed for the cell operating on methane and air, and laboratory operation over 3500 hours is reported. The developers emphasize that considerable engineering and system development must be done before potential advantages and costs for commercial or industrial applications

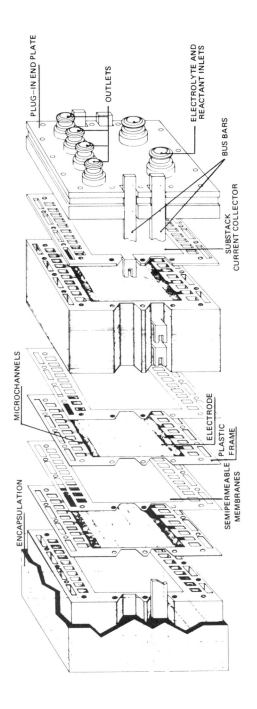

PLUG–IN END PLATE

OUTLETS

ELECTROLYTE AND
REACTANT INLETS

BUS BARS

SUBSTACK
CURRENT COLLECTOR

MICROCHANNELS

ELECTRODE

PLASTIC
FRAME

SEMIPERMEABLE
MEMBRANES

ENCAPSULATION

FIGURE 43.–Alsthom compact hydrazine fuel cell stack.

can be assessed. The companies are considering third-party licenses to accelerate this work.

FUEL CELL COSTS

Although it is difficult to establish reliable cost figures for contemporary fuel cells, some approximations may be made. Fabrication costs for aerospace fuel cells lie in the range $100 000 to $400 000 per kilowatt, the former figure reflecting the cost of more recent designs. Fuel cells developed for military applications are estimated (ref. 11) to cost about $30 000 per kilowatt, with a figure of $10 000 per kilowatt considered a feasible goal. It seems probable that these high figures are a reflection of the limited quantities produced and the requirements for compact, lightweight devices in both applications. In contrast, developers are believed to have set a goal of $100 to $300 per kilowatt for stationary hydrocarbon-burning powerplants in the 10- to 15-kW range, while some economists (ref. 27) are of the opinion that fuel cell powerplants cannot attain economic parity in low- to medium-power (20 to 200 kW) commercial applications unless the investment cost drops to about $10 to $30 per kilowatt. These costs are summarized in figure 44, from which it is obvious that drastic cost reductions are necessary if the fuel cell is to achieve general application.

Two expensive elements in contemporary fuel cells are electrodes and the catalysts incorporated into them, while complex assembly techniques add further to their cost. Current design practices use several innovative techniques that significantly reduce costs, and these are worth examining at this point.

Four approaches may be taken to reducing catalyst costs; the use of less expensive catalysts, more efficient utilization of those employed, and reduction in the amount of catalyst used (catalyst loading and use of a more effective catalyst). Considerable effort has been expended in the search for cheaper catalysts (i.e., cheaper than the commonly used platinum), and alloys of gold, palladium, and other noble metals have been found to be useful in certain applications. No real breakthrough in catalyst cost reduction has been announced, although it is possible that such advances have been made by private concerns. Such discoveries would be regarded as proprietary.

Reductions have been made in the amount of catalyst used in fuel cells by putting it only where needed and using it more efficiently. Figure 45 illustrates how this might be done in a sintered electrode. In early electrodes, catalysts were mixed with the electrode material as shown in figure 45a. Only the surface of each catalyst granule can contribute to the fuel cell reaction so the majority of it is wasted. Likewise, the catalyst located at the outer faces of the electrode is exposed only to the reactant or the electrolyte, but not to both at once where the reaction takes place. Consequently, it too is wasted. By coating inert granules with a thin layer of catalyst and confining these active granules

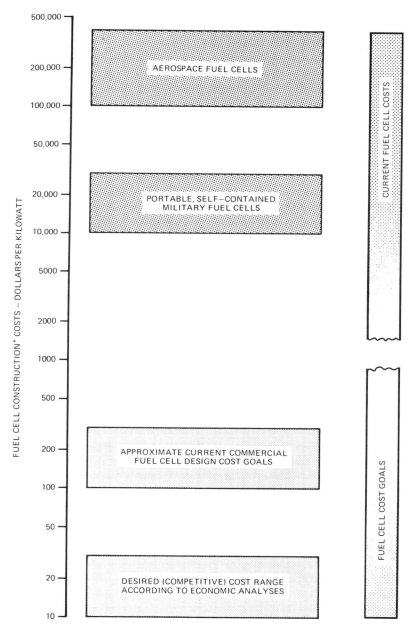

FIGURE 44.–Cost summary.

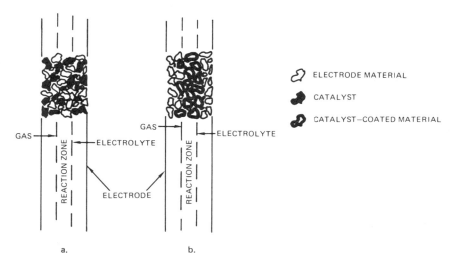

a.   b.

FIGURE 45.—Reduction in catalyst inventory by coating and localization.

to the reaction zone of the electrode (fig. 45b), the amount of catalyst used is considerably reduced without any loss in reactivity.

As understanding of the fuel cell improves and construction experience grows, cheaper electrodes will become possible. Reduction in the complexity and number of process steps during electrode construction has already yielded significant cost reduction in existing fuel cells, and careful design of the electrode and its mounting frame may greatly simplify the assembly of the fuel cell stack. When these techniques are employed in conjunction with relatively large-scale production, cost reductions on the order required are not entirely infeasible.

CHAPTER 7

Applications of Fuel Cells

INTRODUCTION

The relatively high cost of the fuel cell as a power-generation device has limited its application so far to special circumstances having requirements that the fuel cell was able to satisfy, usually by virtue of its high efficiency and consequent low weight, low volume, or low specific fuel consumption. Thus, as a power supply for submersibles, spacecraft, and remotely located repeater stations, it offers special advantages that offset its high cost and other shortcomings. These same advantages have led to the consideration of fuel cells in a number of other specialized applications including portable power supplies and biomedical power devices. Some of these are listed in table 3 as special-purpose applications.

Although the fuel cell finds most immediate application in these specialized areas, it could play more general roles, providing some of the shortcomings can be eliminated. The general-purpose requirements in table 3 are more difficult to meet, particularly regarding economy and lifetime. However, more general applications represent very large markets in comparison with the limited-production special applications. That factor has already prompted the investment of large sums of money in research and development for vehicular propulsion and domestic power.

In most of the proposed applications the fuel cell would function as a power-conversion device, as might be expected. In others, however, the improvements in ion-exchange and electrocatalysis technologies would be exploited not in power-conversion techniques but in the purification or concentration of liquids and gases. In this way, elements of fuel cell technology might be employed as oxygen generators or concentrators in hospitals and aircraft; as dialysis membranes in artificial kidney machines; and in environmental control systems as air cleaners and dehumidifiers, water purifiers, and perhaps as desalination plants.

Fuel cells are currently being operated in or developed for a number of diverse applications. In none of these is the fuel cell a production unit, but rather an engineering model being used to determine the nature and extent of the problems encountered in practical operation and to examine the feasibility, from a technical and economic aspect, of using fuel cells in each role.

An examination of some of these projects is of value, since it illustrates the types of problems that must be overcome and the very different approaches

TABLE 3.—*Potential Fuel Cell Applications*

SPECIAL–PURPOSE

Remote Power

Communications repeaters
Automatic weather/oceanographic
  stations
Navigational aids

Pipeline cathodic corrosion protection
  and instrumentation
Remote signal and beacon devices
Off-shore platforms

Emergency and Standby Power

Hospitals
Civil defense installations
Radio, television, and telephone
  services

Police stations
Fire and intrusion protection
Aircraft

Portable Power

Two-way communications
Lighting
Heating

Search and rescue
Battery charging

Propulsion

Underwater rescue and exploration
Silent power for search and rescue
  vessels

Forklift trucks
Off-road vehicles
Special low-pollution vehicles

Other

Biomedical power
Emergency oxygen for hospitals,
  aircraft

Desalination
Dialysis (artificial kidney machines, etc.)
Environmental control

GENERAL–PURPOSE

Utility Power

Domestic power supplies
Commercial and industrial installations

Power distribution sites
Central generating plant
Peak demand power storage

Propulsion

Low-pollution, low-noise urban
  automobiles
Hybrid power plant highway vehicles

Electric drives for boats
Locomotives
Mass transit vehicles

Recreation

Personal portable power for beach, mountains, etc.
Transportable power for camping, trailers, etc.
Silent power for naturalists, fisherman

that each application requires. The examples chosen do not comprise an exhaustive list of current applications but rather are selected to illustrate the variety in requirements, environments, and power levels under consideration. The first is an outstanding example of a specialized application, the proposed use of a fuel cell as a biomedical powerplant to drive an artificial heart. It vividly illustrates the extreme diversity of potential applications and at the same time provides insight into the problems that must be faced in adapting fuel cells to unusual environments.

The second example describes an effort to develop and evaluate a fuel cell suitable for use in the home. Trial installations have already been made at the time of writing, and the results of these tests may well decide the future of fuel cells in this type of role.

Finally, the application of fuel cells to general automotive propulsion is examined through two examples. The first describes the development of a sophisticated hydrogen-oxygen-fueled system by General Motors incorporating several advanced technological concepts. The second example reviews a more successful, if less spectacular, "do-it-yourself" effort using a combination of hydrogen-air fuel cells and lead-acid batteries.

A FUEL CELL ARTIFICIAL HEART POWER SUPPLY

Blood pumps to assist or replace the heart have been the subject of considerable development effort for several years, and used with some success in animal and clinical experiments (ref. 28). For use over extended periods and during heightened activity, the provision of a suitable power source is a significant problem. To permit the patient to lead a normal life, the power source must be implantable within the body, or must store energy periodically transmitted into the body, preferably through the skin. This problem is being addressed on a broad front by a number of technical approaches. Candidate power sources under consideration include batteries charged by percutaneous transformers, thermoelectric generators powered by isotope heat sources, piezoelectric actuators, reciprocating engines, and fuel cells.

Design Considerations

Investigators have examined (ref. 29) the problem of powering an artificial heart by an implanted fuel cell, and have defined some of the problems inherent in such a project (refs. 30, 31). The limitations of an implanted fuel cell, together with the desirable redundancy of two power sources, have led to the consideration of a hybrid fuel cell/battery system (refs. 31, 32).

The output of an implantable fuel cell for this purpose should be 4 to 5 watts, with peak power requirements (up to 10 watts) being met by a supplementary and backup nickel-cadmium battery. To be implantable the device must occupy a volume of no more than 250 cc (15 in.^{3}) and weigh less than 1.4 kg (3 lb). It must be made from blood- and tissue-compatible materials and must not give off unmanageable quantities of heat or waste products or products that are toxic. Finally, it must operate on reactants that are available within the body.

Performance Limitations

Opinions differ on the design of the fuel cell, but there is general agreement on the reactants that it must use. Glucose is regarded as the best available fuel, since it is plentiful and readily oxidized. Oxygen from the bloodstream is usually considered as the oxidizer and blood plasma as the electrolyte.

Five problems are encountered immediately:

(1) Glucose and oxygen is not a particularly high-energy combination in a fuel cell because complete oxidation represented by $C_6O_6H_{12} + 6H_2O \rightarrow 6CO_2 + 24 H^+ + 24 e^-$ does not occur in practice; instead gluconic acid is the byproduct, yielding only two electrons:

$$C_6O_6H_{12} \rightarrow C_6O_6H_{10} + 2H^+ + 2e^-$$

(2) The plasma is neutral (pH = 7.4), giving rise to high concentration gradients due to its poor buffering capacity and slowing the cathode reaction, which progresses much more rapidly in acid or alkaline conditions.

(3) Solubility of oxygen from oxyhemoglobin in blood plasma is poor and results in very low concentrations, about 2 percent by weight, of the available oxidizable organic fuel species.

(4) Catalysts that are best suited to activating the glucose oxidation reaction are susceptible to poisoning by proteins in the blood plasma.

(5) The presence of both fuel and oxidizer in the supply stream may give rise to opposing potentials at the cathode if the fuel is allowed to react there also, further reducing its already poor performance.

Not much can be done about limitations (1) and (2). Glucose and oxygen represent the best available reactants, and must be accepted despite poor performance. The neutrality of the plasma cannot be altered, since the body vigorously opposes any change in pH by several mechanisms.

Approaches to designing a fuel cell with the desired performance have addressed some of the other limitations. To overcome the low oxygen concentration (3), the use of an air-breathing cathode has been suggested (ref. 31), in which air from outside the body would be caused to flow through the cell in a pulsating mode. A small balloon implanted on the opposite side of the diaphragm from the air inlet would act as a pump for this purpose. The possibility of bacterial ingress and subsequent infection is a danger with this approach. Other workers (ref. 29) have proposed the use of flow-through electrodes to reduce the mass transport problems inherent in surface contact electrodes due to limitation (2). Fuel reactions at the cathode (5) might be overcome by using a selective catalyst that supports only the required reactions, but such a catalyst has not been identified.

A general design goal for the fuel cell has been a current density of about 4 to 5 mA/cm² (projected area) at 0.5 to 0.6 volt. This figure would permit the generation of the required power in the available volume, assuming a total electrode thickness of about 1 mm (1/25 in.). Difficulty has been experienced in attaining and maintaining this current density.

A Design Concept

A somewhat different approach to the problem has been taken by Dr. Jose Giner and coworkers at Tyco Laboratories. Accepting some of the inherent limitations in an implantable fuel cell, this team has established a design goal of only 1 mA/cm², having determined to their own satisfaction, by experiment and analysis, that such a goal is achievable (ref. 32). It is proposed to make up the loss in performance by using extremely thin cells about 250 μ (about 1/100 in.) thick (1 μ = one micron = 1/1000 millimeter). The construction of such cells has verified the feasibility of the concept and tests are currently under way on experimental cells.

The concept proposes the use of glucose and oxygen as the reactants in a hybrid fuel cell/battery system, the goal being a 5-watt fuel cell occupying about 250 cc (15 in.³). The peculiar characteristic of the cell is in its configuration (figure 46).

Blood is supplied through specially constructed channels lying between adjacent cells. Both electrodes are faced with selective membranes that allow only glucose through to the anode and only oxygen to the cathode. The blood channels are molded into the oxygen membrane so that the cell benefits from additional oxygen extraction area. There are thus five components in intimate contact with each other: a glucose-selective permeable membrane, a porous glucose electrode (anode), an electrolyte matrix or separator, an oxygen-electrode (cathode), and an oxygen-selective permeable membrane incorporating the blood supply channels.

The advantages claimed for the concept are that the blood does not contact the electrodes, thereby avoiding clotting problems and catalyst poisoning, and that the desired performance may be attained at low current densities (due to the high packing factor) and without any major technical breakthrough.

Cell Construction

Oxygen electrodes for the cell are formed from PTFE-bonded platinum black with a flat gold grid embedded as a current collector. The gold grid is prepared by photoetching techniques similar to those employed in the

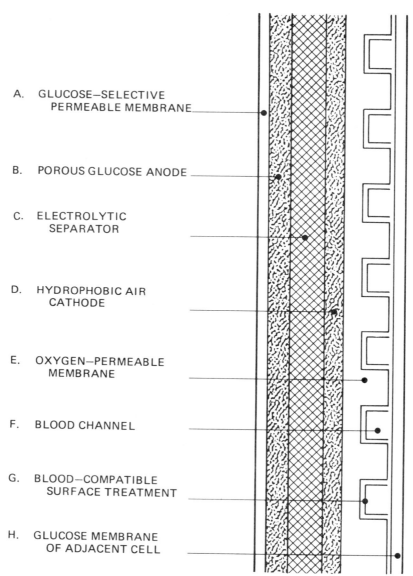

A. GLUCOSE–SELECTIVE
   PERMEABLE MEMBRANE

B. POROUS GLUCOSE ANODE

C. ELECTROLYTIC
   SEPARATOR

D. HYDROPHOBIC AIR
   CATHODE

E. OXYGEN–PERMEABLE
   MEMBRANE

F. BLOOD CHANNEL

G. BLOOD–COMPATIBLE
   SURFACE TREATMENT

H. GLUCOSE MEMBRANE
   OF ADJACENT CELL

FIGURE 46.–Magnified cross-section of a single cell of artificial heart power supply (blood flow perpendicular to plane of paper).

manufacture of printed circuits for electronics. To make the electrode, PTFE is sprayed onto aluminum foil and sintered. A mixture of platinum black and PTFE is then sprayed over this first layer, the gold grid pressed into it, and the remaining platinum/PTFE mix applied. The electrode is then dried and sintered, and the aluminum foil etched away in dilute KOH. The resulting electrode has a thickness of 150 to 230 μ (6 to 9 mils; 1 mil = 1/1000 in.) and a catalyst loading of 13 to 17 mg/cm^2.

Glucose electrodes have been made both as separate components and as films formed directly on the separator material. Independent electrodes are formed by pasting a mix of platinum black and asbestos onto a gold grid formed as for the cathode. They have thicknesses of 100 to 127 μ (4 to 5 mils) and catalyst loading of 9 mg/cm^2. Alternative construction uses 90 μ (3.5 mils) separator material onto which gold is evaporated, followed by the deposition of platinum black. This results in an electrode/separator combination 100 μ (4 mils) thick with 13 mg of platinum per cm^2. When the independent electrodes are used, separator materials 13 μ (0.5 mil) thick are employed.

Glucose permeable membranes of a cellulose material 13 μ (0.5 mil) thick have been used. Collagen membranes 25 μ (1 mil) thick have also been considered.

Oxygen membranes of commercially available dimethylsilicone 25 μ (1 mil) thick have been used as independent components, and alternate membranes of dimethylsilicone-polycarbonate copolymers have been formed directly on the back of the oxygen electrode.

The blood channel structure required for the cell has been formed by two processes; molding of silicone rubber and hot-pressing of PTFE. Both techniques require a mold of the channel structure, which has been made both by precision machining and photoetching techniques. A minimum groove size of 100 μ (1/250 in.) has been selected based on the size of the largest white blood cells (20 μ) and from practical considerations of construction and pressure loss.

Figure 47a shows a magnified cross-section of the channel structure formed by molding silicone rubber. In figure 47b, the channels formed by pressing porous PTFE are shown in a scanning electron micrograph. Good structural integrity and uniformity are displayed in both techniques, and both can be covered with an ultrathin layer of dimethylsilicone-polycarbonate copolymers as a blood-compatibility treatment.

By combining techniques it has been possible to construct integrated multielement units. A PTFE-bonded platinum electrode was formed on the back of a PTFE channel-structure component. The front of the channel structure was then spray-coated with the oxygen permeable membrane. The integral membrane/channel structure/electrode unit is shown in cross-section in figure 47c. It is claimed that such techniques hold promise for reducing the overall cell thickness.

The components currently employed result in a cell thickness of about 400 to 500 μ. With refinement the goal of 250 μ is believed to be attainable. In table 4 the goals for individual component thicknesses are listed and the dimensions of the fuel cell array given.

FUEL CELLS

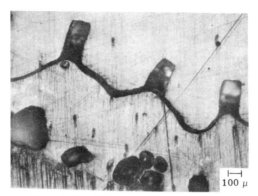

a. Cross-Section of Channels Molded in Silicone Rubber.

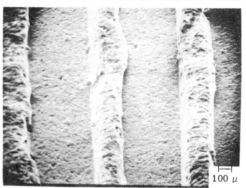

b. Channels Formed by Pressing Porous PTFE
(polytetrafluoroethylene).

c. Cross-Section Through Integral Membrane/Channel
Structure Electrode Unit.

FIGURE 47.—Blood channel construction techniques.

TABLE 4—*Implantable Fuel Cell Design Parameters*

Component	Thickness, μ
O_2 – membrane	12
O_2 – electrode	50
Separator	22
Glucose electrode	40
Glucose–membrane	20
Blood channel	100
Cell total thickness (goal)	244

Cell size	= 10 cm × 5 cm
200 cells @ 250 μ	= 5 cm
Cell stack volume	= 10 cm × 5 cm × 5 cm = 250 cc
Exchange surface	= 200 × 10 cm × 5 cm = 10 000 cm²
Current @ 1 mA/cm²	= 10 A
Power @ 0.5 V	= 5 watts

Cell Performance

Tests to date have proven the concept feasibility, but current densities achieved so far are well below the goal of 1 mA/cm². In addition, slow degradation in the performance of the glucose electrode has been observed due to byproduct contamination, but it has been shown that the original electrode activity is restored by short-term polarization. In an implanted fuel cell, this might be achieved by connecting the supplementary nickel-cadmium battery directly across the fuel cell for a short time. This would have to be done, of course, when the patient was resting since power to the artificial heart would be momentarily reduced or interrupted.

It is suspected that glucose and/or other oxidizable products are diffusing to the PTFE/platinum cathode and being oxidized, lowering the potential of the electrode and reducing the amount of oxygen available for the reaction. This may be reduced either by using an oxidation catalyst that is inactive to glucose (such as gold black or gold-based alloy blacks), or by the use of a separator which does not permit the passage of the interfering species. In selecting a separator, a tradeoff must be made between low transport of interfering reactants and high ion mobility.

FUEL CELLS FOR DOMESTIC POWER SUPPLY

Introduction

The vision of a fuel cell that could provide electricity for domestic consumption spurred much of the development effort between 1890 and 1950 (see ch. 2). In 1897, Dr. W. A. Jaques published (ref. 33) data on a domestic fuel cell that he had developed based on the earlier work of Bequerel and

Jablochkoff. His cell, enclosed in a massive brick structure, operated on carbon and air at a reported efficiency of 82 percent. It was later revealed that the performance was due to the formation of hydrogen by an electrolyte-anode reaction, and that the real efficiency was in fact much lower. Moreover, the cell used pure carbon rather than the economical coal fuel for which it was intended.

Coal-fired fuel cells have been studied since Jaques' work using pure coal dust, but with only limited success. With the changing emphasis on fuel reserves, interest has naturally turned to fuel cells burning hydrocarbon fuels. The technical problems experienced in building this type of cell are discussed in chapter 5. However, the problem is not solely a technical one, for if fuel cells are to attain widespread use on the domestic power market they must be economically competitive and socially acceptable. Many believe the fuel cell holds promise in both these areas.

Its theoretically higher efficiency in comparison with thermal dynamic systems is the basis on which economic superiority might be attained, but the realization of this potential is not simple. The most economic fuels are not those the fuel cell is best able to use, and most current manufacturing techniques result in fuel cells that are expensive pieces of equipment. To these factors must be added the requirements of long life and reliable unattended operation common to all domestic appliances. The economics of fuel cell applications have been studied in detail (refs. 27, 34), and these factors are clearly recognized. Not so clearly appreciated are the less tangible, but equally important, factors surrounding the social acceptability of the fuel cell. Here again it holds advantages over competitive methods of power generation—in theory, if not in practice. Higher efficiency means better utilization of fuels and, therefore, conservation of natural resources. The efficiency of the fuel cell reaction also implies more complete combustion and, thus, exhaust products that are low in pollutants. Direct conversion from chemical energy to electricity should result in less waste heat (another environmental pollutant) and possibly freedom from the noise and vibration inherent in reciprocating and rotating converters.

However, the highly developed hydrogen-oxygen fuel cell that embodies these characteristics to a large degree is in conflict with the economic requirements of an inexpensive machine using cheap fuels. When a fuel cell is built to use cheap fuels, it loses some of its inherent advantages. Its efficiency and lifetime are reduced, its pollutants (thermal and gaseous) tend to increase, and it requires auxiliary components that generate some noise and vibration.

Despite these problems, the potential benefits of a fuel cell domestic power system have encouraged continuing appraisals.

Domestic Fuel Cell Trials

One such appraisal resulted in 1967 in the formation of a consortium of gas utility companies known as the Team to Advance Research for Gas Energy

Transformation (TARGET). The consortium formulated a three-phase, 9-year program with the ultimate goal of establishing a fuel cell energy service, should such a service prove to be attainable. Pratt & Whitney Aircraft was selected as the prime contractor for the program.

Phase I, which explored the technical and economic aspects of the service and established requirements, was completed in 1969. Phase II, in progress at this time (August 1972), includes continued technology development and the production of about 60 experimental powerplants for field testing. These trial units are being used in TARGET's Comprehensive Installation Program, during which installations are being made in single-family homes, apartments, stores, restaurants, office buildings, and at industrial sites. In addition, fuel cell powerplants will be installed at two electric system substations. The performance of the fuel cell powerplant will be monitored over a period of about 3 months at each site under actual service conditions. The purpose of these trials is to obtain essential data to define the technical, economic, and business factors affecting the operation of a fuel cell energy service. It is hoped to identify potential problems in relation to building and utility codes, insurance, reliability and maintenance, response to peak load demands, and other factors.

The PC-11 powerplant designed and built by Pratt & Whitney is rated at 12-1/2-kW nominal power output and is roughly the size of a household furnace unit (fig. 48). The powerplant consists of three elements: a reformer, a fuel cell, and an inverter. The fuel cell and reformer are housed in a single unit (fig. 49), and the inverter is a separate, slightly smaller unit.

The powerplant operation is represented schematically in figure 50. Methane enters the reformer where it is converted to hydrogen and carbon dioxide. This gas mixture is fed to the fuel cell anode, and air is supplied to the cathode. Direct current power from the fuel cell is converted to alternating current in the solid-state inverter to match the household power requirements.

The fuel cell uses phosphoric acid electrolyte immobilized in a matrix-type separator between the electrodes. The use of an acid electrolyte avoids the problems of carbonate formation inherent in alkaline electrolyte cells and eliminates the need for a scrubber to remove the carbon dioxide in the reformed or "processed" fuel. The electrolyte matrix is contained between thin, flexible electrodes in a picture frame gasket (fig. 51). The cells thus formed are stacked between molded separator plates that form the reactant supply channels. Details of electrode construction and the catalyst type(s) and loading are not available, as this information is proprietary. It is claimed that the package volume of the fuel cell reformer may be significantly reduced by rearrangement of the components and some minor redesign. The developers say that if the powerplant is put into commercial service this unit will occupy approximately one quarter the volume of the present unit. A size comparison of the trial unit and the "production" unit may be made from figure 52.

Spokesmen for TARGET are cautious in making predictions about the future of the fuel energy service, saying only that if the program is successful

FIGURE 48.—PC-11 12-1/2-kW hydrocarbon fuel cell powerplant. (Reformer and fuel cell are in the left-hand unit, inverter on the right.)

such a service might be implemented about 1975. The ultimate application of the fuel cell is considered to be in a "total energy and environmental conditioning" (TEEC) role, in which the system would provide not only electrical energy but also heat; would humidify and purify the air; and would possibly be used as a waste processor. It is felt that such a system might be available at the end of this decade. These claims are made with caution, however. TARGET and Pratt & Whitney have invested $50 million in the first two phases of the program and expect to invest much more if the decision is made to continue with Phase III. This commitment reflects the potential benefits that might be expected to accrue to a viable system, but the developers stress that many problems remain unsolved and many questions unanswered at this time.

AUTOMOTIVE POWER APPLICATIONS

Introduction

Growing concern over the air pollution contribution of the conventional automobile in the midsixties (ref. 35) was accompanied by a search for alternatives to the gasoline engine (ref. 36). Among the solutions proposed was a return to the electrically powered automobile (refs. 37, 38), and this has

FIGURE 49.—PC-11 unit with cover removed showing fuel cell (left) and reformer.

resulted in an evaluation of several technological innovations that could make that goal achievable. The fuel cell is one of the devices considered for this application.

The use of a fuel cell as a vehicular propulsion power unit is not new, although the field of demonstration has usually been restricted to off-road vehicles (agricultural and construction machinery, forklift trucks) or special-purpose commercial vehicles with limited range requirements (delivery vehicles,

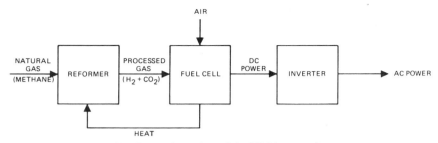

FIGURE 50.—Operation of the PC-11 powerplant.

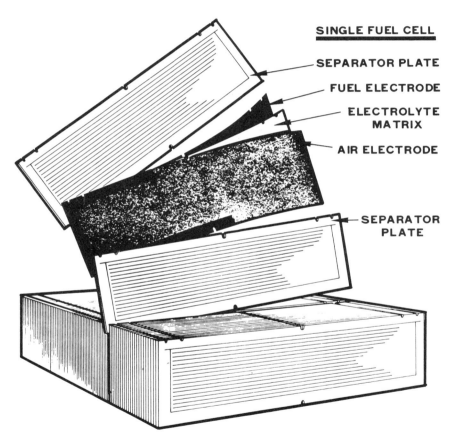

FIGURE 51.—Typical PC-11 fuel cell assembly.

short-haul transportation, etc.). The extension of fuel cell power to private automobiles is recognized as a serious challenge, and a number of analyses have indicated that to provide the same performance as a conventional

ADVANCED POWERPLANT 1971 DESIGN

TARGET FIELD TEST POWERPLANT 1968 DESIGN

FIGURE 52.–Size comparison between 1968 field test fuel cell and 1971 advanced compact model.

internal combustion engine in a regular size vehicle, a fuel cell with state-of-the-art capabilities would have to weigh more than the car (ref. 39).

However, it is pointed out that the conventional automobile is grossly over-powered, the engine being sized to satisfy the peak, rather than the average, power demand. Since this factor contributes to air pollution, it is reasoned that a reduction in performance is a price that must be paid for cleaner air. It is not clear whether the driving public is prepared to accept this penalty, but if one accepts reduced automobile power as a premise, then perhaps fuel cells could be engineered into effective powerplants for private vehicles.

Taking another approach, several workers have proposed hybrid power-plants comprising fuel cells and batteries—the batteries providing the peak power and the fuel cells acting as charging units during low power demand periods. If this approach is combined with an acceptance of somewhat lower performance, the fuel cell might provide an engineering solution to the problem.

Several vehicular fuel cell and fuel cell/battery power systems have been built and demonstrated, but mainly for military vehicles (ref. 40) and special-purpose vehicles (ref. 41) with limited range requirements. Two applications to passenger-type vehicles are worthy of note, however. The contrast between these two endeavors is significant; the first being an all-out assault on the problem by General Motors Corporation, the second a private venture by a fuel cell research technologist.

A Fuel Cell-Powered Van

In 1964, the Power Development Group of GMC began a program (ref. 42) to build and test several electric vehicles with the objective of establishing development goals for various drive components such as electric motors, motor controls, and power sources. One of the vehicles was to be powered by a fuel cell system without batteries.

A GMC van weighing 1476 kg (3250 lb) (fig. 53) was selected for the test vehicle because it offered ample space for the fuel cell system which was expected to be bulky. The major parts of the system (fuel cells and drive train) were accommodated under the floor, but the reactant storage tanks were located within the body in a specially constructed space between two bench seats (fig. 54).

System Description

The drive motor was a specially developed 125-hp, four-pole, three-phase, oil-cooled induction motor designed to operate at 13 700 rpm. A sophisticated electronic control system using oil-cooled silicon-controlled rectifiers was employed. These components represented an attempt to apply the most advanced technology to the program, an objective considered in keeping with the use of a fuel cell power source.

FIGURE 53.—A fuel cell-powered van.

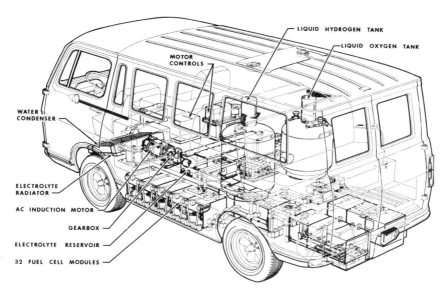

LIQUID HYDROGEN TANK

LIQUID OXYGEN TANK

MOTOR
CONTROLS

WATER
CONDENSER

ELECTROLYTE
RADIATOR

AC INDUCTION MOTOR

GEARBOX

ELECTROLYTE RESERVOIR

32 FUEL CELL MODULES

FIGURE 54.—Phantom view of electrovan showing arrangement of major components.

The fuel cell system was assembled by GMC from modules developed and built by Union Carbide Corporation (refs. 43, 44). Operating on hydrogen and oxygen, the system had a rated output of 32 kW and a peak power capability of 160 kW. It used aqueous potassium hydroxide electrolyte that was circulated through the cell and through a heat exchanger to provide thermal control. Water was carried from the cells in the hydrogen stream and removed in a condenser. Normal operating temperature was 65° to 70° C. Figure 55 is a schematic of the system.

The fuel cell stack comprised 32 modules, each having a nominal power rating of 1 kW. Each module contained 68 cells connected in 17 series strings of four parallel cells. The 321 cm^2 (0.346 ft^2) electrodes were of 0.2-mm (0.008-in.) thick porous nickel, to one surface of which was applied 0.4 to 0.5 mm (15 to 20 mils) of graded layers of activated carbon, wetproofing agents, and catalysts. The design of this type of electrode is described in reference 45.

Cell construction is detailed in figure 56a. One anode and cathode were bonded to a polysulfone frame to form an electrolyte sandwich, 1.27-mm (50-mil) cell spacing being maintained by a plastic mesh. Molded into the frame were six longitudinal passages for supply and return of hydrogen, oxygen, and electrolyte. Narrow passages connected these manifolds with the interelectrode cavities. The dimensions of the passages were chosen carefully to provide sufficient electrical resistance to limit intercell leakage currents through the electrolyte and ensure uniform flow. Cell sandwiches thus formed were stacked anode-to-anode and cathode-to-cathode, spaced, and sealed by a neoprene gasket forming the hydrogen and oxygen cavities. Epoxy-fiberglass end, top,

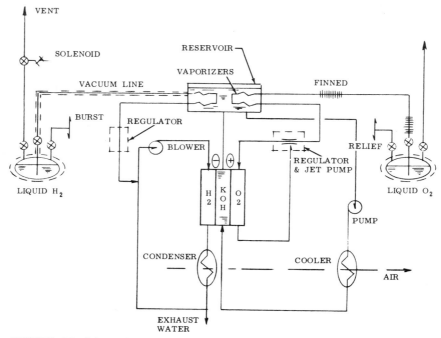

FIGURE 55.—Schematic of the electrovan fluid system showing four fluid loops: hydrogen, oxygen, electrolyte and air.

and bottom plates provided mechanical pressure to seal the stack. The sides of the stack were potted in epoxy resin after making the intercell electrical connections (fig. 56b). The technique resulted in a clean, compact, leakproof stack of approximately 0.028 m³ (1 ft³).

System Problems

Among the major problems encountered were the weight of the fuel cell system and the high parasitic loads encountered. The complete fuel cell system weighed 1534 kg (3380 lb), more than the basic GMC van in which it was installed. The dry modules accounted for 40 percent of this weight, the accessories 44 percent, and the electrolyte 16 percent. A detailed weight summary is given in table 5. The parasitic losses amounted to 5.4 kW, 3 kW being required to drive the accessories (pumps, fans, etc.) and 2.4 kW being lost in electrolyte leakage currents.

Performance

The fuel cell-powered van weighed 3220 kg (7100 lb), more than twice the weight of the standard version. Although full power tests were not conducted

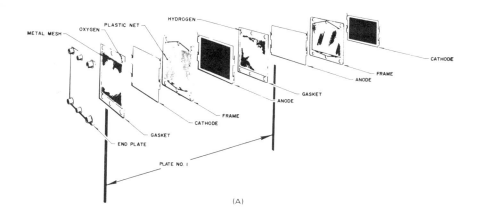

(A)

(B)

FIGURE 56.—Electrovan fuel cell. (A) Exploded view of fuel cell. (B) 1-kW fuel cell module.

TABLE 5.—*Fuel Cell Powerplant Principal Subsystems
Weight and Volume Breakdown*

Fluid system	lb	%	Electric system	lbs	%
Hydrogen loop	112	7.6	Modules.............	1345	70.4
Oxygen loop	134	9.1	Racks and plumbing ...	200	10.5
Electrolyte loop	160	10.9	Main power	88	4.6
Electrolyte	550	37.5	Auxiliary power	86	4.5
Hydrogen blower	36	2.4	Control–safety	57	3.0
Heat exchanger package	105	7.2	Instrumentation	135	7.0
Fuel supply package* ..	372	25.3			
			Total	1911	100%
Total	1469	100%			

		Weight			Volume	
	lb	%	lb/kW	cu ft	%	ft³/kW
Modules, dry	1345	39.8	8.4	18**	23	.12
Auxiliaries, fluid–electric	1485	44.0	9.3	60**	77	.37
Electrolyte	550	16.2	3.4	- - -	- - -	- - -
Total fuel cell powerplant	3380	100	21.1	78	100	.49

*Less vaporizers
**External volume of module enclosures is 36 ft³

on the road, the performance of the test vehicle was estimated from laboratory tests on a similar power system. These indicated that the vehicle's top speed would be similar to that of the production van, but acceleration and range would be only 60 percent of standard. These figures are summarized in table 6.

The designers concluded that the program had demonstrated the feasibility of building fuel cell vehicular powerplants, and noted that the overall thermal efficiency of the system was roughly twice that of a gasoline engine. Problems encountered were summarized as follows:

(1) Heavy weight and large volume

(2) Short lifetime

(3) Costly components and materials

(4) Complicated and lengthy startup and shutdown procedures

(5) Removal and disposal of exhaust products—byproduct water, gas bleeds, and gas leaks

(6) Sensitivity to contamination both in the gases and the electrolyte

(7) Complexity of the three separate fluid systems—hydrogen, oxygen, and electrolyte

(8) Difficult temperature control requirements

(9) New safety problems—high voltages, electrolyte leaks, hydrogen leaks, and possible collision hazard

TABLE 6.—*Comparison of Performance and Weights—Electrovan versus GMC Production Van*

	Electrovan	GMC van
Total vehicle weight	7100 lb	3250 lb
Fuel cell power	3380 lb	
Electric drive	550 lb	
Powertrain total	3930 lb	870 lb
Performance 0–60 mph	30 sec	23 sec
Top speed	70 mph	71 mph
Range	100-150 miles	200-250 miles

(10) Critical gas-electrolyte pressure balance during transient conditions and on grades or curves

It is possible that some of these problems resulted from the ambitious goal of the project, which was to duplicate the performance of a regular vehicle using only fuel cells as the power source. The project also involved several technological innovations not directly associated with the fuel cell (e.g., ac motor and control system), and the fuel cell system is believed to have been the most powerful ever assembled up to that time.

A Fuel Cell-/Battery-Powered Automobile

A different approach was taken (ref. 24) in a later application of fuel cells to passenger vehicles. Dr. Karl Kordesch, one of the developers of the Union Carbide cells used in the Electrovan, set out to build what he terms a "city car." He did not try to duplicate the performance of a general-purpose automobile, but to construct a vehicle for city driving or suburban commuting.

Dr. Kordesch's car is a 906-kg (2000-lb) vehicle based on a 1961 British Austin A-40 chassis, two-door, four-passenger sedan (fig. 57). The powerplant consists of a dc electric motor and a hybrid fuel cell/battery energy source. The 6-kW fuel cell, which is based on the electrodes used in the GMC Electrovan, uses an air-breathing cathode, obviating the need for oxygen tanks, piping and control. The polarization experienced by this type of cathode under heavy load can be tolerated because peak power demands are satisfied by the lead-acid battery. The project is significant in that the vehicle has been operated on public roads as a functional means of transportation for a period of more than a year (ref. 45), and the powerplant control has been reduced to a simply operated fail-safe system.

FIGURE 57.—A fuel cell-powered automobile.

System Description

The electric motor and lead battery system are installed under the hood (fig. 58). The motor is a Baker, series-wound dc motor with two field windings similar to that used in forklift trucks. It is rated at 7.5-kW continuous, 20- to 25-kW peak power, 4000 rpm maximum speed, and weighs 82 kg (180 lb). The power train is the standard four-speed manual transmission fitted to the A-40.

Seven 12-volt, 84 ampere-hour lead-lead dioxide (lead-acid) batteries are installed above and beside the motor and connected in series. The batteries are standard SLI (starting, lighting, ignition) types weighing 21.4 kg (47 lb) each for a total of 150 kg (330 lb). A charging unit installed in the car can replenish the batteries from a regular household 117-volt ac supply, and automatically disconnects at 10 to 15 percent overcharge. An ampere-hour counter installed under the instrument panel in the car registers the instantaneous state of charge of the batteries at all times.

The fuel cell system is installed in the trunk of the car and consists of 120 cells in 15 modules arranged in three blocks as shown in figure 59. The fuel cell operates at a nominal 90 volts and produces about 6 kW of power. The cell is supplied with pure hydrogen from high-pressure tanks and with air by means of a blower. Air is passed through a transparent trough filled with sodalime to remove the CO_2. The trough is mounted above the fuel cell stack just inside the rear window. Aqueous potassium hydroxide electrolyte is circulated through the fuel cell and through a heat exchanger (fig. 60). The electrolyte is pumped from a reservoir under the cell and remains in this reservoir when the system is not operating. This is an important functional feature, since it allows the cell to be shut down completely. As a result, no parasitic currents are

FIGURE 58.—Installation of electric motor and batteries.

FIGURE 59.–Fuel cell system installed in truck and hydrogen stored in roof-mounted cylinders.

drawn, no reactants are required to maintain electrode potentials, and hydrostatic pressure is removed from the electrodes. The system features a nitrogen purge circuit used during startup and shutdown. This circuit connects automatically in response to underpressure or overtemperature signals from the fuel cell so that in the event of a major leak or short circuit the system automatically shuts down. There is no danger of the vehicle losing power unexpectedly due to this sequence, since the batteries will continue to power the car to a place where it may be stopped safely. As a further safety feature, the inlet of the air blower feeding the fuel cell is placed inside the car so that any gas leaks are returned immediately to the cell. The weight of the fuel cell is 59 kg (130 lb), and the accessories (pumps, tanks, blowers, etc.), which are all commercially available units, weigh 23 kg (50 lb).

The hydrogen supply is stored in six steel cylinders at 1290 N/cm^2 (1865 psi) on the roof of the car (figs. 57 and 59). A regulator outside the car reduces this figure to about 38 N/cm^2 (55 psi), and the pressure is further reduced at the fuel cell by a low-pressure regulator within a range of 0.05 N/cm^2 to 0.30 N/cm^2 (2 to 12 in. of water). The cylinders hold a total of 18.7 m^3 (660 ft^3) of hydrogen and weigh 12.7 kg (28 lb) each for a total of 76 kg (168 lb). The tanks are fitted with high-pressure and high-temperature relief plugs, and the installation follows all regulations for the transportation of hazardous materials. The designer notes that compliance with these regulations is only

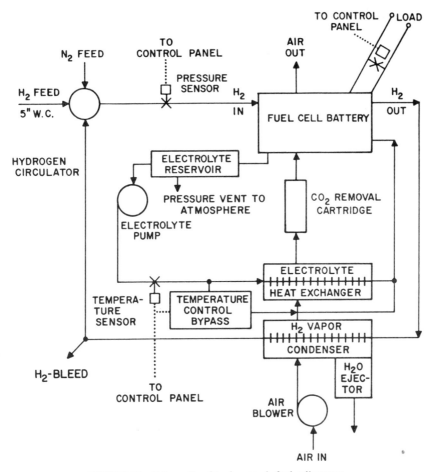

FIGURE 60.–Schematic of hydrogen-air fuel cell system.

required for commercial transportation of such materials, and further that the day-to-day transportation of gasoline in regular automobile tanks appears to be at least as dangerous as the transport of hydrogen gas in steel high-pressure cylinders. The cylinders are refilled by connecting the manifold on the roof to any 1380 N/cm^2 (2000 psi) storage facility. Flexible steel armored tubing with handwheel connectors permits refilling in a few minutes without any tools.

The electrical circuit is shown schematically in figure 61, which shows that the fuel cells and the lead-acid batteries are connected all the time via a diode preventing backcharging. However, for starting purposes this diode can be bridged to help the fuel cell battery come up in voltage uniformly, without cell reversal. This is a very important feature; when an electrically series-connected fuel cell battery with parallel electrolyte feed is supplied with the active gases, some cells will obtain the fuel first and drive the others into reverse. When this

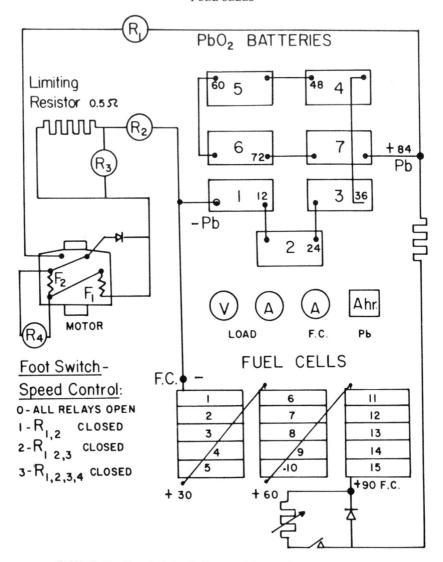

FIGURE 61.—Electrical circuit diagram of fuel cell/battery-powered car.

happens it can take hours to "right them up" with the help of auxiliary batteries. In this system the lead battery voltage, applied at a time when the hydrogen manifolds are still filled with nitrogen, assures the correct polarity by producing hydrogen and oxygen (in small amounts) through electrolysis.

The starting sequence is semiautomatic, governed by an additional safety circuit that does not allow hydrogen to enter the manifolds unless the electrolyte is circulating. Overtemperature sensors at critical points shut the

TABLE 7.— *System Startup Sequence*

Sequence switch position	Fuel cell system status	Functions effected in sequence
0	Off	
1	Starting	Open nitrogen valve, purge system rapidly; bridge diode.
2	Starting	Start electrolyte pump and air blower; open bleed valve; open H_2 supply valve.
3	Starting	Disconnect diode bridge resistor; bleed reduced to fraction of use rate.
4	Operating	Normal mode, all accessories energized.
5	Shutdown	All accessories deenergized; open N_2 valve; open bleed valve; purge system rapidly.
6	Off	(Corresponds to position 0)

system down and fill it with nitrogen when needed. To start the car all the operator has to do is turn the keyswitch. The vehicle may immediately be driven on the batteries while the fuel cell is brought online by means of a sequence switch, a procedure that takes 1 to 2 minutes (table 7). The completion of each step is indicated by a panel light, and the sequence switch is manually indexed to the next position. At position two the hydrogen supply is connected via a hand valve mounted between the sun visors over the driver's head. The sequence could readily be made fully automatic; manual operation has been retained in this experimental vehicle to facilitate study of the startup sequence. Emergency or regular shutdown is straightforward as indicated in table 7; the sequence switch is simply turned to position five and shutdown is automatic.

Speed control is achieved by means of a gas pedal-type control that closes a series of relays in sequence (fig. 61) and by gear-shifting in the normal manner. In operation, the car behaves very much like its gasoline-powered predecessor; inside, it even sounds the same, since most of the drive train noise emanates from the gear box, which is retained.

Instrumentation

Instruments keep the operator informed of the system condition at all times. Mounted below the dashboard on the driver's right is a panel of three meters. Two meters display the motor voltage and current; the third meter shows the current being drawn from the fuel cell only. This panel also carries the sequence switch and indicator lights. The ampere-hour counter, which shows the battery condition, is mounted below the panel. A pressure gauge overhead monitors the hydrogen supply, while gauges mounted on each side of the fuel cell, and visible in the rear-view mirror, indicate air-differential and hydrogen supply pressures.

Performance

The behavior of the car during acceleration is depicted in figure 62. Although starting from standstill in top gear gives the most rapid acceleration (20 seconds to 64 km/h (40 mph)), it results in heavy battery drain and must be avoided since the circuit is protected by a 300-A fuse. Using the gearbox to limit current drain results in an acceleration time of approximately 25 to 30 seconds to 64 km/h (40 mph). Load-sharing between the fuel cell and battery occurs naturally due to the different slopes of the polarization curves (fig. 63). Starting from standstill, both battery and fuel cell operate close to full power. At cruising speed the load is shared equally when the battery charge is high, or

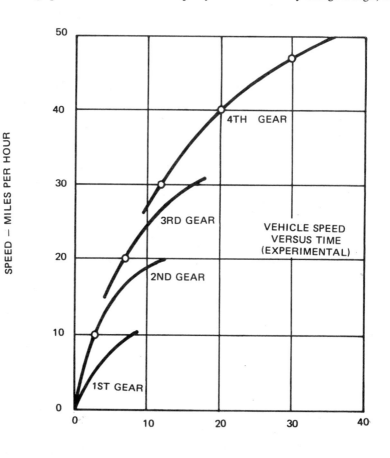

TIME – SECONDS

FIGURE 62.–Acceleration diagram: Time needed to reach certain speed.

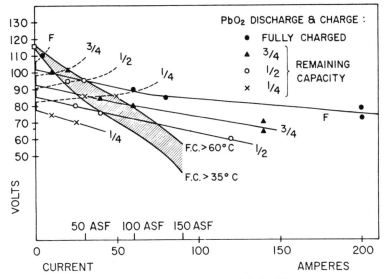

FIGURE 63.–Load-sharing characteristics of fuel cell/battery system.

the power can be supplied solely from the fuel cell when the battery is almost discharged. At standstill the fuel cell pumps energy into the battery at a rate dependent on the state of charge. Experimental data on the load-sharing characteristics are summarized in table 8.

The range of the car has been estimated from partial consumption figures as 320 km (200 mi). This is a significant improvement over battery-only vehicles, which are usually limited to 80 to 160 km (50 to 100 mi). Dr. Kordesch's car, for example, which was previously (1966) operated on lead batteries only, had a range of 80 km (50 mi) in the summer and 48 km (30 mi) in the winter. Operating costs are estimated at 0.5 cents per mile, based on a bulk purchase price of 30 to 40 cents per pound (6.2 m^3 or 220 ft^3) of hydrogen. Based on the delivered price of individual cylinders, it is estimated that the cost would be as much as 5 cents per mile.

Maintenance

Routine maintenance procedures for the car include battery water replenishment and periodic replacement of the sodalime CO_2 scrubber. Water replenishment must be done less frequently than originally anticipated, probably because of good cooling of the batteries by air-flow due to their placement and careful charge control using the ampere-hour counter as a reference. The sodalime is changed twice in about 1 year of operation; and apparently changes are not required more frequently than every 1600 km (1000 mi). Special indicator particles included with the sodalime change color

TABLE 8.—*Load-Sharing of the Hydrogen-Air/Lead
System under Different Operating
Conditions (Experimental Data)*

| Output | | | Pb-battery | | H_2-air | Operating |
kW	V	A	state-of-charge	±A	A	conditions
11.0	85	125	1/1	− 80	45	55 mph 4th gear
9.5	80	115	3/4	− 60	55	52 mph reduced field
8.0	75	105	1/2	− 40	65	48 mph battery temp.
6.5	70	95	1/4	− 25	70	42 mph 65° C
20.0	75	260	1/1	−200	60	Steep hill, 2nd gear
14.0	65	210	3/4	−140	70	or start from stand.
12.0	60	195	1/2	−120	75	Battery Temp. 45° C
8.0	90	90	1/1	− 60	30	45 mph 4th gear
7.0	85	80	3/4	− 40	40	42 mph full field
5.6	80	70	1/2	− 20	50	38 mph battery temp.
4.5	72	60	1/4	0	60	35 mph 65° C
4.0	70	58	1/4	+ 7	65	32 mph 4th gear
3.0	84	35	1/2	+ 8	48	20 mph 3rd gear
2.0	88	22	1/2	+ 13	35	10 mph 2nd gear
0.5	110	5	1/1	+ 5	5	Car stopped.
2.0	100	20	3/4	+ 20	20	Charging depends
2.8	95	30	1/2	+ 30	30	on state of charge
4.2	85	50	1/4	+ 50	50	and temperature

Note: 60-A current equals 100 mA/cm² current density.

when it is saturated, giving a clear visual indication of the need for replacement. Periodic flushing of the fuel cells with water appears to be desirable to remove buildup of dried electrolyte at the gas outlets. The manifolds may be flushed with tap water without danger to the electrodes, which are wetproofed.

The designer reports few problems with the system. The motor and its control circuitry have operated without attention since their original installation in 1966. The batteries have a life expectancy of at least 2 years, and the fuel cells have demonstrated lifetimes of 2000 hours continuous operation, the equivalent of 80 000 to 96 000 km (50 000 to 60 000 mi), in laboratory tests. Experience indicates that this expectancy may be increased under intermittent use conditions.

The only serious problem reported is the development of leaks in the fuel cells, believed to be due to the use of mixture of materials with different thermal expansion rates (nylon, plexiglass, and epoxy). This problem could be solved by using one material throughout for construction, polysulfonates being recommended by the designer. The leaks have not proved catastrophic to either the fuel cell or the environment. Potassium hydroxide does not damage the vehicle body and may be washed off readily with water.

As installed, the fuel cell is quite accessible through the trunk opening of the car (fig. 59) and from inside the car by tilting the rear seat. The underside of the fuel cell may be reached for minor repairs by tilting the cell forward into the body space after removing the seat back.

Future Fuel Cell-Powered Cars

The significant feature of Kordesch's car is its practicality. It represents a low pollution vehicle with useful performance and range and a simply operated, fail-safe system. The technology embodied in the vehicle is quite old, and the designer claims that recent improvements in electrode construction would significantly improve the performance or could be used to extend the range. The use of ammonia as fuel in conjunction with a thermal dissociation unit to convert it to hydrogen has been considered as a means of reducing the fuel tankage volume.

The emphasis of current research in this field is on high-energy batteries (zinc-air, sodium-sulfur, and others) and on low pollution internal combustion engines, the fuel cell receiving little attention in comparison. The selection between these approaches must be made on the basis of detailed technical and economic analyses that are beyond the scope of this survey.

References

1. Grove, W. R.: On Voltaic Series in Combinations of Gases by Platinum. Philosophical Magazine, vol. 14, 1839, pp. 127-130.
2. Grove, W. R.: On A Small Voltaic Battery of Great Energy; Some Observations on Voltaic Combinations and Forms of Arrangement; and on the Inactivity of a Copper Positive Electrode in Nitro-Sulphuric Acid. Philosophical Magazine, vol. 15, 1839, pp. 287-293.
3. Grove, W. R.: On a Gaseous Voltaic Battery. Philosophical Magazine, vol. 21, 1842, pp. 417-420.
4. Mond, L. L.; and Langer, C.: Proceedings of the Royal Society (London), Services, A, vol. 46, 1890, pp. 296-304.
5. Grubb, W. T.: Ion-Exchange Batteries. Proceedings of the 11th Annual Battery Research and Development Conference, Atlantic City, N. J., 1957, pp. 5-8.
6. Austin, L. G.: Fuel Cells–A Review of Government-Sponsored Research, 1950-1964. NASA SP-120, 1967.
7. Kordesch, K. V.: Low Temperature–Low-Pressure Fuel Cell with Carbon Electrodes. Handbook of Fuel Cell Technology, edited by Carl Berger, Prentice-Hall, 1968.
8. Colman, W. P.; Gershberg, D.; Di Palma, J.; and Haldeman, R. G.: Light-Weight Fuel Cell Electrodes. Proceedings of the 19th Annual Power Sources Conferences, May 18-20, 1965.
9. Grubb, W. T.; and Niedrach, L. W.: Batteries with Solid Ion-Exchange Membrane Electrolytes, II. Low Temperature Hydrogen-Oxygen Fuel Cells. Journal of the Electrochemical Society, vol. 107, Feb. 1960, pp. 131-135.
10. Liebhafsky, H. A.: Fuel Cells and Fuel Batteries–An Engineering View. IEEE Spectrum, Dec. 1966, pp. 48-56.
11. Rogers, L. J.: Hydrazine-Air (60/240 watt) Manpack Fuel Cell. Proceedings of the 23rd Annual Power Sources Conference, May 1969, pp. 1-4.
12. Warszawski, B.; Verger, B.; and Dumas, J. C.: Alsthom Fuel Cells for Marine and Submarine Applications. Marine Technology Society Journal, vol. 5, no. 1, Jan./Feb. 1971, pp. 28-41.
13. Adlhart, O. J.; and Terry, P. L.: Ammonia Fuel Cell System. Proceedings of the 4th Intersociety Energy Conversion Engineering Conference, Sept. 1969, pp. 1048-1051.
14. Rothschild: Fuel Cells. Science Journal, vol. 1, no. 1, Mar. 1965, pp. 82-87.
15. Ciprios, G.: The Methanol-Air Fuel Cell Battery. Proceedings of the 1st Intersociety Energy Conversion Engineering Conference, Sept. 1966, pp. 9-14.
16. Poirier, A. R.: Engineering Development of a Direct Hydrocarbon-Air Fuel Cell System. Proceedings of the 1st Intersociety Energy Conversion Engineering Conference, Sept. 1966.
17. Peattie, C. G.: Hydrocarbon-Air Fuel Cell Systems. IEEE Spectrum, June 1966, pp. 69-76.
18. Frysinger, G. R.: Experience with Liquid Hydrocarbon Fuels. Proceedings of the 19th Annual Power Sources Conference, May 1965, pp. 11-13.

19. Juda, W.: A Hydrocarbon-Air Fuel Cell with Molten Alkali-Hydroxide Electrolyte. Proceedings of the Electrochemical Society Meeting, Montreal, Oct. 1968.

20. Dunlop, J. D.; Van Ommering, G.; and Stockel, J. F.: Analysis of the Single-Cell Concept for a Rechargeable H_2-O_2 Fuel Cell. Proceedings of the 6th Intersociety Energy Conversion Engineering Conference, Aug. 1971, pp. 906-917.

21. Giner, J.; Holleck, G.; and Malachesky, P. A.: Research on Rechargeable Oxygen Electrodes. NASA CR-72999, Jan. 1971.

22. Allison, A. J.; Ramakumar, R.; and Hughes, W. L.: Economic High-Pressure Hydrogen-Oxygen Regenerative Fuel-Cell Systems. Proceedings of the 4th Intersociety Energy Conversion Engineering Conference, Sept. 1969, pp. 1042-1047.

23. Durante, Lt. B.; Stedman, J. K.; and Bushnell, C. L.: High Power Density Fuel Cell. Proceedings of the 4th Intersociety Energy Conversion Engineering Conference, Washington, D. C., Sept. 1969.

24. Kordesch, K. V.: Hydrogen-Air/Lead Battery Hybrid System for Vehicle Propulsion. Abstract No. 10, Electrochemical Society, Oct. 1970.

25. Malaspina, F. P.: 30-Watt Metal Hydride-Air Fuel Cell System. Proceedings of the 22nd Annual Power Sources Conference, May 1968, pp. 20-22.

26. Fee, G. G.; and Storto, E.: 20-Amp, 28 Vdc Hydrazine-Air Silent Power Source. Proceedings of the 23rd Annual Power Systems Conference, May 1969, pp. 8-10.

27. Henry, J.; LeFort, R.; LeFeure, D.; and Verstraete, J.: Fuel Cell Economics and Commercial Applications. Handbook of Fuel Cell Technology, edited by Carl Berger, Prentice-Hall, 1968, pp. 496-596.

28. Harmison, L. T.; and Hastings, F. W.: Artificial Heart Program. Proceedings of the Artificial Heart Program Conference, Washington, D.C., June 1969.

29. Beltzer, M.; and Batzold, J. S.: Limitations of Blood Plasma as a Fuel Cell Electrolyte. Proceedings of the 4th Intersociety Energy Conversion Engineering Conference, Washington, D.C., Sept. 1969, pp. 354-360.

30. Messinger, S.; and Drake, R. F.: Trophically Powered Fuel Cell Power Supply for an Artificial Heart. Proceedings of the 4th Intersociety Energy Conversion Engineering Conference, Washington, D.C., Sept. 1969, pp. 361-369.

31. Appleby, A. J.; Ng. D. Y. C.; Wolfson, S. K.; and Weinstein, H.: An Implantable Biological Fuel Cell with an Air-Breathing Cathode. Proceedings of the 4th Intersociety Energy Conversion Engineering Conference, Washington, D.C., Sept. 1969, pp. 346-353.

32. Giner, J.; Holleck, G. L.; Turchan, M.; and Fragala, R.: An Implantable Fuel Cell to Power an Artificial Heart. Proceedings of the 6th Intersociety Energy Conversion Engineering Conference, Boston, Mass., Aug. 1971, pp. 256-266.

33. Jaques, W. W.: Harpers Magazine, vol. 94, 1896, pp. 114-150.

34. Hart, A. B.; and Womack, G. J.: Fuel Cells. Chapman and Hall, 1967, pp. 274-292.

35. U.S. Department of Commerce: The Automobile and Air Pollution. Dec. 1967.

36. Heller, A. N.: An Examination of Alternatives to the Gasoline Automobile. Power Systems for Electric Vehicles, pp. 5-12.

37. Frysinger, G. R.: Fuel Cell—Battery Power Sources for Electric Cars. Power Systems for Electric Vehicles, U.S. Department of Health, Education and Welfare, Apr. 1967, pp. 83-90.

38. Hoffman, G. A.: The Electric Automobile. Scientific American, Oct. 1966, pp. 34-40.

39. Lindgren, N.: Electric Cars—Hope Springs Eternal. IEEE Spectrum, Apr. 1967, pp. 49-60.

40. Dantowitz, P.; and Caddy, L.: A State-of-the-Art Automotive Fuel Cell Power System for Electric Vehicles, U. S. Department of Health, Education and Welfare, Apr. 1967, pp. 297-306.

41. Barak, M.: European Developments of Power Sources for Electric Vehicles. Power

Systems for Electric Vehicles, U. S. Department of Health, Education and Welfare, Apr. 1967, pp. 105-119.

42. Marks, C.; Rishavy, E. A.; and Wyczalek, F. A.: Electrovan–A Fuel Cell-Powered Vehicle. Paper 670176, SAE Automotive Engineering Congress, Detroit, Jan. 1967.

43. Winters, C. E.; and Morgan, W. L.: The Hydrogen-Oxygen Thin Electrode Fuel Cell Module. Paper 670182, SAE Automotive Engineering Congress, Detroit.

44. Wyczalek, F. A.; Frank, D. L.; and Smith, G. E.: A Vehicle Fuel Cell System. Paper 670181, SAE Automotive Engineering Congress, Detroit.

45. Kordesch, K. V.: City Car with H_2-Air Fuel Cell/Lead Battery (One Year Operating Experiences). Proceedings of the 1971 Intersociety Energy Conversion Engineering Conference, Boston, Mass., Aug. 1971, pp. 103-111.

Bibliography

Adlhart, O. J.; and Terry, P. L.: Ammonia Fuel Cell System. Proceedings of the 4th Intersociety Energy Conversion Engineering Conference, Sept. 1969, pp. 1048-1051.

Allison, A. J.; Ramakumar, R.; and Hughes, W. L.: Economic High-Pressure Hydrogen-Oxygen Regenerative Fuel-Cell Systems. Proceedings of the 4th Intersociety Energy Conversion Engineering Conference, Sept. 1969, pp. 1042-1047.

Appleby, A. J.; Ng, D. Y. C.; Wolfson, S. K.; and Weinstein, H.: An Implantable Biological Fuel Cell with an Air-Breathing Cathode. Proceedings of the 4th Intersociety Energy Conversion Engineering Conference, Washington, D.C., Sept. 1969, pp. 346-353.

Archer, D. H.: Fuel Cells for Central Power Generation. ASME Paper No. 67-PWR-10, ASME-IEEE Joint Power Generation Conference, Detroit, Sept. 1967.

Austin, L. G.: Electrode Kinetics and Fuel Cells. Proceedings of the IEEE, vol. 51, Jan.-June 1963, pp. 820-837.

Austin, L. G.: Fuel Cells—A Review of Government-Sponsored Research, 1950-1964. NASA SP-120, 1967.

Barak, M.: European Developments of Power Sources for Electric Vehicles. Power Systems for Electric Vehicles, U.S. Department of Health, Education and Welfare, Apr. 1967, pp. 105-119.

Beltzer, M.; and Batzold, J. S.: Limitations of Blood Plasma as a Fuel Cell Electrolyte. Proceedings of the 4th Intersociety Energy Conversion Engineering Conference, Washington, D.C., Sept. 1969, pp. 354-160.

Bender, R. J.: The Fuel Cell: Commercial in the 70's? Power, Apr. 1971, pp. 60-61.

Bockris, J. O'M.; and Wroblowa, H.: Electrochemical Catalysis. AGARD-NATO Combustion and Propulsion: Colloquium on Energy Sources and Energy Conversion, Agardographs Series, no. 81, 1967, pp. 717-767.

Ciprios, G.: The Methanol-Air Fuel Cell Battery. Proceedings of the 1st Intersociety Energy Conversion Engineering Conference, Sept. 1966, pp. 9-14.

Cohn, E. M.: Electrochemical Space Power Sources. AGARD Space Power Systems, Part 2, 1969, pp. 443-501.

Colman, W. P.; Gershberg, D.; Di Palma, J.; and Haldeman, R. G.: Light-Weight Fuel Cell Electrodes. Proceedings of the 19th Annual Power Sources Conferences, May 18-20, 1965.

Dantowitz, P.; and Caddy, L.: A State-of-the-Art Automotive Fuel Cell Power System for Electric Vehicles. U. S. Department of Health, Education and Welfare, Apr. 1967, pp. 297-306.

Dunlop, J. D.; Van Ommering, G.; and Stockel, J. F.: Analysis of the Single-Cell Concept for a Rechargeable H_2-O_2 Fuel Cell. Proceedings of the 6th Intersociety Energy Conversion Engineering Conference, Aug. 1971, pp. 906-917.

Durante, Lt. B.; Stedman, J. K.; and Bushnell, C. L.: High Power Density Fuel Cell. Proceedings of the 4th Intersociety Energy Conversion Engineering Conference, Washington, D. C., Sept. 1969.

Fee, G. G.; and Storto, E.: 20-Amp. 28 Vdc Hydrazine-Air Silent Power Source. Proceedings of the 23rd Annual Power Systems Conference, May 1969, pp. 8-10.

Frysinger, G. R.: Experience with Liquid Hydrocarbon Fuels. Proceedings of the 19th Annual Power Sources Conference, May 1965, pp. 11-13.

Frysinger, G. R.: Fuel Cell–Battery Power Sources for Electric Cars. Power Systems for Electric Vehicles, U. S. Department of Health, Education and Welfare, Apr. 1967, pp. 83-90.

Frysinger, G. R.: The Economical Fuel Cell. IEEE Spectrum, Mar. 1969, pp. 83-90.

Giacoletto, L. J.: Energy Storage and Conversion. IEEE Spectrum, Feb. 1965, pp. 95-102.

Gidaspow, D.; Baker, B. S.; and Schmidt, T.: Thermal Design of Molten Carbonate Fuel Cells. Proceedings of the 1st Intersociety Energy Conversion Engineering Conference, Sept. 1966, pp. 19-23.

Giner, J.; Holleck, G.; and Malachesky, P. A.: Research on Rechargeable Oxygen Electrodes. NASA CR-72999, Jan. 1971.

Giner, J.; Holleck, G.; and Fragala, R.: An Implantable Fuel Cell to Power an Artificial Heart. Proceedings of the 6th Intersociety Energy Conversion Engineering Conference, Boston, Mass., Aug. 1971, pp. 256-266.

Grove, W. R.: On A Gaseous Voltaic Battery. Philosophical Magazine, vol. 21, 1842, pp. 417-420.

Grove, W. R.: On A Small Voltaic Battery of Great Energy; Some Observations on Voltaic Combinations and Forms of Arrangement; and on the Inactivity of a Copper Positive Electrode in Nitro-Sulphuric Acid. Philosophical Magazine, vol. 15, 1839, pp. 287-293.

Grove, W. R.: On Voltaic Series in Combinations of Gases by Platinum. Philosophical Magazine, vol. 14, 1839, pp. 127-130.

Grubb, W. T.: Ion-Exchange Batteries. Proceedings of the 11th Annual Battery Research and Development Conference, Atlantic City, N. J., 1957, pp. 5-8.

Grubb, W. T.; and Niedrach, L. W.: Batteries with Solid Ion-Exchange Membrane Electrolytes, II. Low Temperature Hydrogen-Oxygen Fuel Cells, Journal of the Electrochemical Society, vol. 107, Feb. 1960, pp. 131-135.

Harmison, L. T.; and Hastings, F. W.: Artificial Heart Program. Proceedings of the Artificial Heart Program Conference, Washington, D. C., June 1969.

Hart, A. B.; and Womack, G. J.: Fuel Cells. Chapman and Hall, 1967, pp. 274-292.

Heller, A. N.: An Examination of Alternatives to the Gasoline Automobile. Power Systems for Electric Vehicles, pp. 5-12.

Henry, J.; LeFort, R.; LeFeure, D.; and Verstraete, J.: Fuel Cell Economics and Commercial Applications. Handbook of Fuel Cell Technology, edited by Carl Berger, Prentice-Hall, 1968, pp. 496-596.

Hoffman, G. A.: Energy Requirements for Electric Automobiles. Proceedings of the 1st Intersociety Energy Conversion Engineering Conference, Los Angeles, Sept. 1966, pp. 368-379.

Hoffman, G. A.: The Electric Automobile. Scientific American, Oct. 1966, pp. 34-40.

Jaques, W. W.: Harpers Magazine, vol. 94, 1896, pp. 114-150.

Juda, W.: A Hydrocarbon-Air Fuel Cell with Molten Alkali-Hydroxide Electrolyte. Proceedings of the Electrochemical Society Meeting, Montreal, Oct. 1968.

Justi, E. W.: Fuel Cell Research in Europe. Proceedings of the IEEE, vol. 51, Jan.-June 1963, pp. 784-795.

Kordesch, K. V.: City Car with H_2-Air Fuel Cell/Lead Battery (One Year Operating Experiences). Proceedings of the 1971 Intersociety Energy Conversion Engineering Conference, Boston, Mass., Aug. 1971, pp. 103-111.

Kordesch, K. V.: Hydrogen-Air/Lead Battery Hybrid System for Vehicle Propulsion. Abstract No. 10, Electrochemical Society Meeting, Oct. 1970.

Kordesch, K. V.: Low Temperature Fuel Cells. Proceedings of the IEEE, vol. 51, Jan.-June 1963, pp. 806-812.

Kordesch, K. V.: Low Temperature–Low-Pressure Fuel Cell with Carbon Electrodes. Handbook of Fuel Cell Technology; edited by Carl Berger, Prentice-Hall, 1968.

Liebhafsky, H. A.: Fuel Cells and Fuel Batteries–An Engineering View. IEEE Spectrum, Dec. 1966, pp. 48-56.

Lindgren, N.: Electric Cars–Hope Springs Eternal. IEEE Spectrum, Apr. 1967, pp. 49-60.

Malaspina, F. P.: 30-Watt Metal Hydride-Air Fuel Cell System. Proceedings of the 22nd Annual Power Sources Conference, May 1968, pp. 20-22.

Marks, C.; Rishavy, E. A.; and Wyczalek, F. A.: Electrovan – A Fuel Cell-Powered Vehicle. Paper 670176, SAE Automotive Engineering Congress, Detroit, Jan. 1967.

Messinger, S.; and Drake, R. F.: Trophically Powered Fuel Cell Power Supply for an Artificial Heart. Proceedings of the 4th Intersociety Energy Conversion Engineering Conference, Washington, D. C., Sept. 1969, pp. 361-369.

Mond, L. L.; and Langer, C.: Proceedings of the Royal Society (London), Services, A, vol. 46, 1890, pp. 296-304.

Peattie, C. G.: A Summary of Practical Fuel Cell Technology to 1963. Proceedings of the IEEE, vol. 51, Jan.-June 1963, pp. 795-806.

Peattie, C. G.: Hydrocarbon-Air Fuel Cell Systems. IEEE Spectrum, June 1966, pp. 69-76.

Poirier, A. R.: Engineering Development of a Direct Hydrocarbon-Air Fuel Cell System. Proceedings of the 1st Intersociety Energy Conversion Engineering Conference, Sept. 1966.

Reid, W. T.: Energy Sources for Electrically Powered Automobiles. Battelle Technical Review, no. 14, pp. 9-15.

Ritchings, F. A.: Raw Energy Sources for Electric Generation. IEEE Spectrum, Aug. 1968, pp. 34-45.

Rogers, L. J.: Hydrazine-Air (60/240 watt) Manpack Fuel Cell. Proceedings of the 23rd Annual Power Sources Conference, May 1969, pp. 1-4.

Rothschild: Fuel Cells. Science Journal, vol. 1, no. 1, Mar. 1965, pp. 82-87.

Smith, A. B.: Fuel Cells–Power for Tomorrow. Radio Electronics, Feb. 1967, pp. 44-47.

Spadone, D. M.: Power for Deep-Submergence Vehicles. Astronautics and Aeronautics, July 1967, pp. 76-79.

Spring, K. H., ed.: Direct Generation of Electricity. Academic Press, 1965.

U. S. Department of Commerce: The Automobile and Air Pollution, Dec. 1967.

Vogely, W. A.: Analytical Uses of Energy Balances. IEEE Spectrum, May 1969, pp. 57-63.

Warszawski, B.; Verger, B; and Dumas, J. C.: Alsthom Fuel Cells for Marine and Submarine Applications. Marine Technology Society Journal, vol. 5, no. 1, Jan./Feb. 1971, pp. 28-41.

Watson, R. G. H.: Fuel Cell Reactant Properties. AGARD-NATO Combustion and Propulsion: Colloquium on Energy Sources and Energy Conversion, Agardograph Series, no. 81, 1967, pp. 681-707.

Winters, C. E.; and Morgan, W. L.: The Hydrogen-Oxygen Thin Electrode Fuel Cell Module. Paper 670182, SAE Automotive Engineering Congress, Detroit.

Wyczalek, F. A.; Frank, D. L.; and Smith, G. E.: A Vehicle Fuel Cell System. Paper 670181, SAE Automotive Engineering Congress, Detroit.

Yeager, E.; and Kozawa, A.: Kinetic Factors in Fuel Cell Systems: The Oxygen Electrode. AGARD-NATO Combustion and Propulsion: Colloquium on Energy Sources and Energy Conversion, Agardograph Series, no. 81, 1967, pp. 769-793.

Sources of Further Information

Readers wishing to explore the technology of fuel cells more thoroughly may find the following list of information sources a useful supplement to the bibliography.

BOOKS

The following books were published during the period 1961 to 1971. Because of the rapid advances made in the technology then, the most recently published books are listed first.

Baker, B. S.; and Gould, R. F.: Fuel Cell Systems - 2. (Advances in Chemistry Series No. 90), American Chemical Society, 1969.

Bockris, J. O'M.; and Srinivasan, T.: Fuel Cells: Their Electrochemistry. McGraw-Hill, 1969.

Breiter, M. W.: Electrochemical Processes in Fuel Cells. Springer-Verlag, 1969.

Ranney, M.: Fuel Cells. Noyes, 1969.

Berger, C.: Handbook of Fuel Cell Technology. Prentice-Hall, 1968.

Liebhafsky, H. A.; and Cairns, E. J.: Fuel Cells and Fuel Batteries: A Guide to Their Research and Development. Wiley, 1968.

Austin, L. G.: Fuel Cells–A Review of Government-Sponsored Research, 1950-1964. NASA (SP-120), 1967.

Hart, A. B.; and Womack, G. J.: Fuel Cells: Theory and Application. Chapman and Hall, 1967.

Bagotsky, V. S.; and Vasil'Ev, Y. B.: Fuel Cells: Their Electrochemical Kinetics. Plenum Pub., 1966.

Baker, B. S.: Hydrocarbon Fuel Cell Technology: A Symposium. Academic Press, 1966.

Halacy, D. S., Jr.: Fuel Cells: Power for Tomorrow. World Pub., 1966.

Klein, H. A.: Fuel Cells, Lippincott, 1966.

Williams, K. R.: Introduction to Fuel Cells. Elsevier, Amsterdam, 1966.

American Chemical Society. Fuel Cell Systems. Advances in Chemistry Series No. 47, American Chemical Society Pub., 1965.

Mitchell, W., Jr.: Fuel Cells. (Chemical Technology, Vol. 1), Academic Press, 1963.

American Chemical Society. Fuel Cells. Vol. 2, Young, G. J., Ed., Reinhold, 1962.

Justi, E. W.; and Winsel, A. W.: Cold Combustion Fuel Cells. Franz Steiner, Wiesbaden, Germany, 1962.

PERIODICALS

No periodical currently published is devoted specifically to fuel cells. However, several regularly scheduled conferences and meetings deal with fuel cell technology, and the proceedings form a valuable source of information on current developments.

Power Sources

A Power Sources Symposium (PSS) is held annually to present and discuss results of Government, university, and industrial investigations in the power field. The conference is sponsored by the Power Sources Division, Electronic Components Laboratory, U.S. Army Electronics Command, Fort Monmouth, N.J. The proceedings of the Conference are published and distributed by the PSS Publications Committee, P. O. Box 891, Red Bank, N.J. 07701.

Intersociety Energy Conversion Engineering Conference (IECEC)

The IECEC meets in August or September each year to present the results of the engineering and application aspects of nonconventional energy conversion. It is cosponsored by the seven member societies listed below. Each society in turn has published the proceedings, in the order listed.

American Society of Mechanical Engineers (ASME), 1967
Institute of Electrical and Electronics Engineers (IEEE), 1968
American Institute of Chemical Engineers (AIChE), 1969
American Nuclear Society (ANS), 1970
Society of Automotive Engineers (SAE), 1971
American Chemical Society (ACS)

The 1972 conference will be hosted by the ACS in San Diego, September 25-29. The conference chairman is Mr. A. T. Winstead of ACS. The AIAA will be host to the 1973 conference.

Electrochemical Society Meetings

The Electrochemical Society (ECS) meets in the spring and fall each year. Papers presented include those on fuel cell technology and applications. For information contact: The Electrochemical Society, 30 East 42nd Street, New York, New York.

International Power Sources Symposium (IPSS)

The IPSS (until 1964, the International Symposium on Batteries) is held once every 2 years at Brighton, England. The Symposia are sponsored by the British Joint Services Electrical Power Sources Committee and the proceedings are edited by D. H. Collins and published by Pergamon Press.

Annual CITCE Meetings

The International Committee of Electrochemical Thermodynamics and Kinetics (Comité International de Thermodynamique et de Cinetique Electrochimique, CITCE) meets annually. Papers presented at the conference are published in the committee's journal, *Electrochimica Acta*, by Pergamon Press.

U.S. GOVERNMENT PRINTING OFFICE : 1973 O—499-155

2591-31607
5-02